Brera

Complete guide to the works in the gallery

introduction by

Luisa Arrigoni

SCALA

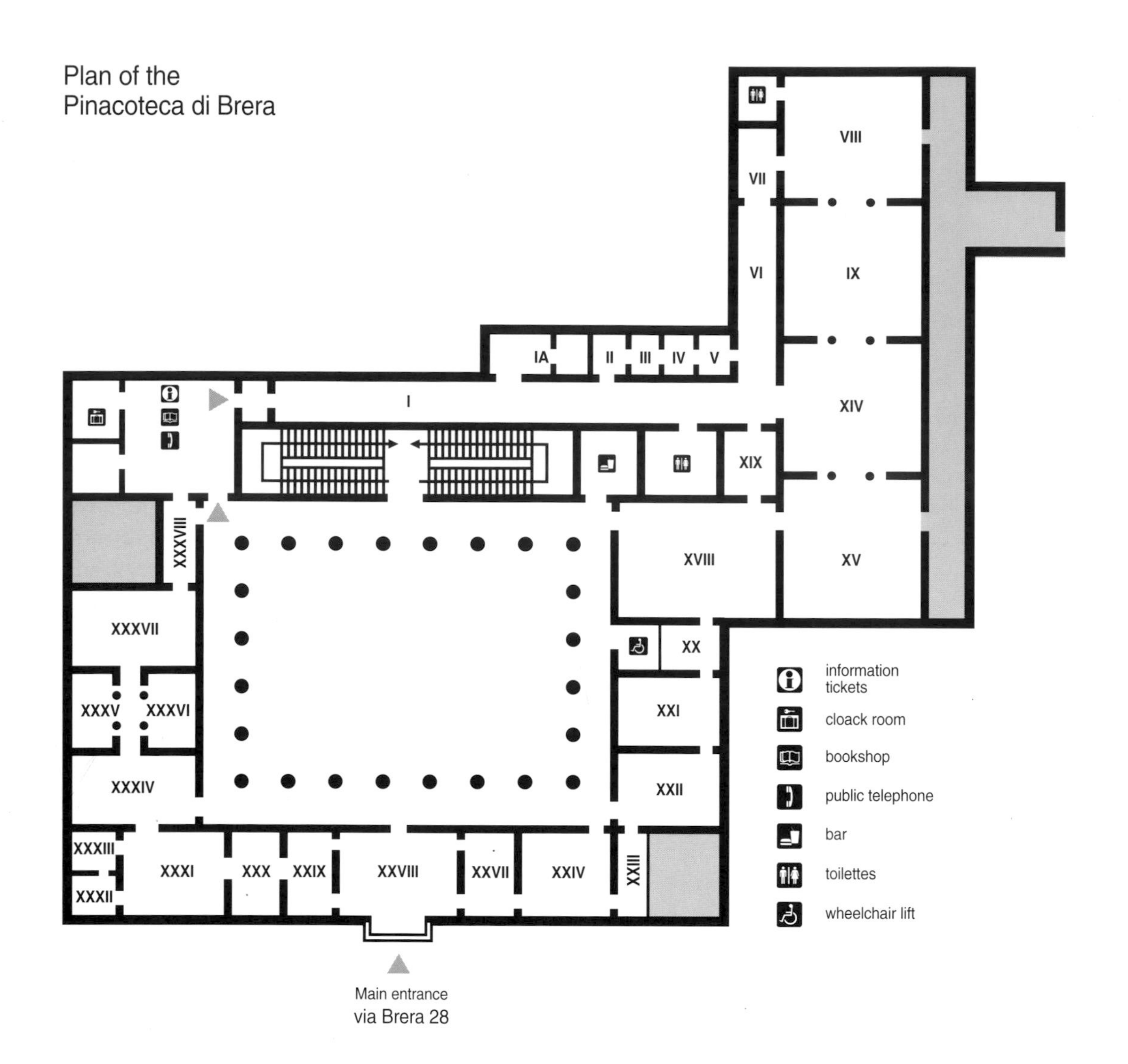

Introductory texts to the rooms: Nadia Righi
Catalogue: Lorenza Targetti

The sections of the catalogue reflect the arrangement in May 1997 and are organized in clockwise fashion, from left to right starting at the entrance to each room.

Introduction

Anyone approaching the Palazzo di Brera from Piazza della Scala gets a view of the building that does not differ greatly from the appearance it would have had at the time of the Art Gallery's inauguration, on August 15, 1809.

At that date the fine fourteenth-century church of Santa Maria di Brera, which used to face onto the small square in which the rather unassuming monument to Francesco Hayez stands, had already been incorporated into the nobly austere palace, distinguished by the contrast in color between the dark red of its brick facing and the gray stone of its window sills, copings and stringcourse moldings. The church's Gothic facade with its alternating black and white courses, portal and sculptures by Giovanni di Balduccio had already been demolished to increase the size of the four square rooms that would be used to house the Art Gallery.

The destruction of this facade, a monument of an age that was extremely rare in Milan, caused great sorrow to "antiquarians," "connoisseurs" and "lively intelligences," as it was put at the time, and stripped the palace of a fundamental aspect of its origins.

Before it became the seat of not only the Art Gallery, but also the Academy of Fine Arts, National Library of Brera, Astronomical (now just Meteorological) Observatory, Lombard Institute of Science and Letters and Botanical Garden, the Palazzo di Brera had been, in different form and dimensions, the mother house of the Order of the Humiliati. This was a semi-monastic religious community famous for the working of wool, which produced cloth that was much appreciated throughout the Western world. The monastery and its workshops had been constructed on the edge of the medieval city, on a piece of uncultivated land called a *brayda* (whence the names Brera and Braidense). Later the church was added, initially very simple but then modernized in the Gothic style and embellished in the mid fourteenth century. In 1571, at the urging of Cardinal Carlo Borromeo, Pope Pius V ordered the abolition of the Humiliati and the monastic complex was handed over to the Jesuits to set up a school and a college that would be consonant with the wealth and importance of Milan. So work began on the design of a new building modeled on the Collegio Borromeo in Pavia, and lasted from 1573 to 1590. Owing to difficulties in raising money and problems with the acquisition of adjoining land, necessary to straighten the boundaries and permit the construction of rooms with a regular shape, the building work went slowly. It was not until 1627, after Francesco Maria Richini had redesigned and expanded Martino Bassi's initial project, that the building of the new monastery was joined by the first two schools, "capacious and majestic ... comfortable and splendid." After the forced interruption of the outbreak of plague in 1630, design and construction resumed and in 1651 the general of the order gave his approval to the final project, whose fulcrum was a large rectangular courtyard with two rows of loggias embellished with Serliane and linked by a monumental staircase. On Richini's death in 1658, supervision of the construction work passed to his son Gian Domenico and the architects Gerolamo Quadrio and Giorgio Rossone, who were very active in Milan in those years. Work proceeded according to the original design for about a century and the building assumed noble and austere forms in keeping with Lombard baroque architecture.

When the Society of Jesus was dissolved in 1773 as a consequence of the wave of anticlericalism that swept through Europe with the change in relationship between State and Church, the College of Brera, with its new and prestigious astronomical observatory, its botanical garden and the whole of the Jesuit library, reverted to state ownership. Maria Theresa of Austria, who for years had been engaged in a general plan for the reform of educational institutes in Milan, acquired the property and revenues with satisfaction and immediately entrusted Giuseppe Piermarini, architect and inspector-general of state constructions, with the renovation of the palace. In 1776 the institutes were integrated by the foundation of the Academy of Fine Arts and the Patriotic Society, which later became the Lombard Institute of Science and Letters, while the library was expanded. By 1785 the upper story of the facade was at last complete and, having rejected the idea of placing the main entrance beside the church of Santa Maria di Brera, Piermarini built a monumental neoclassical portal on Via Brera, with an arch, columns and a sturdy balcony on top.

With the creation of the Academy and above all the appointment of Carlo Bianconi, a Bolognese student of anatomy and collector who was a friend of Francesco Algarotti and pupil of Ercole Lelli, as secretary in 1778, a collection of engravings, drawings, plaster casts, copies and a few paintings was assembled for the instruction of pupils. Although this first group of

works, enriched in 1799 with canvases by Pierre Subleyras, Pompeo Batoni, Giuseppe Bottani, Filippo Abbiati, Carlo Francesco Nuvolone and Stefano Legnani, has been seen as the origin of the Pinacoteca di Brera, the history of the Art Gallery does not really start until 1800-01, with the reconstitution of the Cisalpine Republic and the appointment of Giuseppe Bossi, a painter, writer, expert on art, collector and friend of Canova and Angelica Kauffmann, as secretary.

In 1802 Bossi was joined by Andrea Appiani, also a painter: the official portraitist of Napoleon and a friend of men of letters and politicians, he served as a powerful and highly active commissioner of Fine Arts. Bossi's attention was concentrated on the program of renewal of academic teaching, which led to the drawing up of new and modern statutes in 1803, in which the Art Gallery was mentioned for the first time as an institution of fundamental importance to academic studies. Bossi carried out an intense activity of cultural promotion, whose results were formally celebrated in 1806 by the first public exhibition and the award of prizes to works submitted to the competitions that had been staged that year. This was recorded in a printed guide that described the rooms on the first floor and is still an indispensable source of information on the changes that were made over that brief span of time. Appiani, in his capacity as commissioner for requisitions, supervised the arrival of paintings from the various departments into which first the Cisalpine Republic and then the kingdom of Italy were subdivided. He made continual journeys of reconnaissance, drawing up lists of deserving works which would then be sent to Brera. In 1807, after Bossi had left the post of secretary of the Academy, he became curator of the Art Gallery and left a significant mark on the cultural policy of the Napoleonic period through his brilliant handling of his role as a collector on behalf of the State.

The courtyard of Palazzo di Brera.

In 1805, the year that Napoleon was crowned king of Italy, a decree issued by the Ministry of the Interior on August 2 declared that all the requisitioned works would be assembled at the Academy of Fine Arts and divided into three categories: those by more famous artists would be put on show in the gallery, those of lesser interest used for exchanges and those of little value transferred to churches lacking decoration that had put in requests for them.
Thus dozens and dozens of works started to arrive: initially from secularized churches and monasteries in Lombardy, they were later joined by hundred of paintings brought from the various departments of the kingdom. Many came from Veneto where Pietro Edwards distinguished himself in their selection, but an equally large number were from the former papal domains.
Napoleon's directive, based on ideological principles rooted in the French Revolution, called for the formation of large national galleries as a means of education and a symbol of the nation's greatness and history. At Brera this took the concrete form of a living monument to the civil prestige of his political power. Thus one of the largest collections of art in Italy, on a par with those of the Uffizi and the Vatican, was formed almost at a stroke, over the space of just a few years.
In the face of such a massive influx of works, almost all of them large altarpieces whose imposing solemnity was to become a permanent connotation of the museum, the problem of space soon became a pressing one. To give the gallery more room and a better organization, the decision was taken in 1808 to build a second floor in the church of Santa Maria di Brera, at the height of the aisles. The alterations, carried out to a design by Pietro Gilardoni, architect of the Ministry of the Interior, created a large vaulted space on the ground floor for the Museum of Lombard Antiquities and four large rooms with columns, illuminated by windows and skylights set in the middle of the ceilings, on the second floor for the Art Gallery. Inaugurated on August 15, 1809, Napoleon's birthday, they were called the "Napoleonic rooms" and were destined to become the heart of the museum. Still known by the same name, they have remained unaltered ever since. It has recently been demonstrated that a total of 139 paintings were initially put on show, in three rooms (the fourth had not been finished yet). They included Carpaccio's *Scenes from the Life of the Virgin* and *Preaching of Saint Stephen*, Veronese's *Agony in the Garden*, Daniele Crespi's *Last Supper*, Genga's *Sant'Agostino Altarpiece*, Moretto's *Assumption*, Giovanni Bellini's *Greek Madonna*, Titian's *Saint Jerome*, Bramantino's *Crucifixion*, the *Sforza Altarpiece*, and the *Preaching of Saint Mark* by Gentile and Giovanni Bellini, to mention just a few.
But the plunder continued and the number of works in the Pinacoteca di Brera increased rapidly up until 1813. By the end of that year, according to the so-called "Napoleonic Inventory" (which had been used since 1808 to register all the paintings entering Brera in chronological order), it had risen to a total of 889 panels, canvases and detached frescoes. Not all of these additions were the result of requisitions and suppressions: the representative character of the museum in civil life was already encouraging donations and acquisitions. In 1804 Francesco Melzi donated the *Triptych with Saint Helen* by Palma il Vecchio (believed at the time to be the work of Lorenzo Lotto) and in 1806 Eugène Beauharnais, to underline the importance that the French government attached to the new gallery, acquired for Brera a number of works from the Sannazzari collection that had been bequeathed to the Ospedale Maggiore in Milan. These included

the section on Venetian painting, previously dominated by religious paintings of large size. He was also responsible for the completion of Vincenzo Foppa's *Polyptych of the Graces*, through his acquisition of the predella (1912), and a number of purchases made with the money raised by the exhibition of Italian painting staged in London in 1930. His initiatives aroused the interest of Milanese patrons of the arts, and in 1926 this was channeled into the Association of Friends of Brera and the Milanese Museums, the first body of this kind to be set up in Italy. From that time on it has made a distinguished contribution to the museum, with donations that include Caravaggio's *Supper at Emmaus*, Silvestro Lega's *The Pergola*, Segantini's *Spring Pastures* and Giovanni da Milano's *Christ the Judge*, among many others.
During the Second World War there was a new dispersion and the empty gallery was used to house exhibitions organized by Giuseppe Bottai's Center of Action for Contemporary Art. Partly destroyed by Allied bombing in 1943, the museum was rebuilt between 1947 and 1950 under the direction of Fernanda Wittgens and with the assistance of Gian Alberto dell'Acqua. In 1950 it was solemnly inaugurated, rapidly becoming a symbol of the desire for rebirth and determination to reconstruct that marked postwar Italy. The grandiose decoration given to the museum by the architect Piero Portaluppi over this period, enhanced by the use of old marble from the Opificio delle Pietre Dure in Florence, was juxtaposed with the modern style of Franco Albini's wing, set alongside the Napoleonic rooms, with its small and elegant rooms filled with light.
In the fifties and sixties the collections were further enlarged by a constant series of donations, often connected with the cultural activity of the Friends of Brera. These included Morazzone's *Saint Francis in Ecstasy*, Bonifacio Bembo's *Saints Alexis and Julian*, Umberto Boccioni's *Self-Portrait*, Cariani's *Resurrection*, Baronzio's *Scenes from the Life of Saint Columba*, Niccolò di Pietro's *Coronation of the Virgin*, and Giacomo Ceruti's two *Porters*.
The seventies saw the beginning of a series of problems that have beset the museum right down to the present day. In 1974 Franco Russoli, appointed director the previous year, drew attention to the very grave crisis in which the Art Gallery found itself, due to a failure to maintain the structures and systems installed after the war and a shortage of staff and space. The museum was closed and only the most famous works remained on display in the last few rooms, in an exhibition significantly entitled "For Brera" that was intended as a denunciation of the problems it faced.
From that moment on Russoli committed himself to the project of a "Greater Brera." This entailed using Palazzo Citterio, an eighteenth-century building almost next door to the Palazzo di Brera that had been acquired in 1972, to house all the structures and services that could not be fitted into the crowded former home of the Jesuits. These ranged from facilities for educational activities (including lecture rooms and an auditorium) to structures for the reception and guidance of visitors, a cafeteria and a bookstore, in addition to workshops and spaces for temporary exhibitions and the newly acquired permanent collections of modern art. In 1976 in fact, Brera, which had hitherto restricted its attention entirely to the art of the past, opened its doors to the twentieth century thanks to the donation made by Emilio and Maria Jesi. This brought to the museum over fifty first-rate works (a further sixteen would be added in 1984) by Italian artists of the early twentieth century, from Boccioni to Carrà, Modigliani, Morandi, Sironi, De Pisis, Scipione, Mafai, Marino Marini and Arturo Martini. Two other Milanese collectors, Riccardo and Magda Jucker, lent the museum a collection of around twenty fundamental Futurist paintings (in 1993, after a series of hitches, the Jucker collection was acquired by Milan's Civic Museum of Contemporary Art).
Russoli's untimely death (in 1977) left the project at an embryonic stage. Under the direction of Carlo Bertelli, the museum was reopened and enlarged with the acquisition of a new wing located in what was once the eighteenth-century astronomer's residence, facing onto the Botanical Garden. A number of innovative steps were taken on many fronts, though the time required for their realization has not always been in keeping with the purposes for which they were intended. The Soprintendenza per i Beni Ambientali e Architettonici, which is responsible for the restoration of the building, carried out work in the corridor leading to the Napoleonic rooms and room XXII, reconstructing the ceilings and reopening the windows in an attempt to return them to the condition they were in at the time of the Jesuits. The small rooms built by Piero Portaluppi to house the "masterpieces" of Bramante, Piero della Francesca and Raphael were united to form a single large hall with a flat ceiling designed by Vittorio Gregotti and Antonio Citterio. At the same time the organization of the collections was modified, often in a significant manner and with a number of extremely interesting but short-lived initiatives. These included the recreation, though only partial, of Giuseppe Bossi's Cabinet of Portraits of Painters, the display of fifteenth-century polyptychs from the Marche in the astronomer's apartment along with Venetian paintings of small size from the same century and, shortly afterward, the exhibition of the Jesi and Jucker collections in an elegant and highly restrained setting designed by Ignazio Gardella.

The gallery that houses the Jesi donation.

Since 1989, after much of the museum had been closed and stripped because of problems with the heating and lighting systems and the renovation of Palazzo Citterio, where the work begun by Franco Russoli had been left largely unfinished, had been entrusted to James Stirling, work has started on a complex program of rationalization and modernization of the technical plant, from climate control to lighting, security and fire-fighting systems. The job has been entrusted to Vittorio Gregotti, who has produced a plan of functional reorganization whose first fruits are now visible in the large Napoleonic rooms, in a series of small side rooms that are used to display so-called gold-ground paintings and Venetian pictures from the fifteenth-sixteenth century and in the room housing polyptychs from the Marche.
The new arrangement of the museum has gone hand in hand with an extensive reorganization of the collections. A number of paintings recovered from external deposits have now been put on show, modifying the appearance of various rooms in the Picture Gallery. These range from Luca Giordano's *Holy Family with Saint Anthony of Padua* to Ludovico Carracci's *Preaching of Saint Anthony Abbot*, Francesco Salviati's *Lamentation*, Jacopo Palma il Vecchio's *Adoration of the Magi* and others. They also include several recent gifts and acquisitions: from Giuseppe Pellizza da Volpedo's *The Stream* to Joseph Heintz the Younger's *Allegory of Love*, Gentile da Fabriano's *Crucifixion* and Giampietrino's *Madonna della Mela*, to mention just a few.

Luisa Arrigoni
Director of the
Pinacoteca di Brera

THE MOCCHIROLO CHAPEL

The first thing you come to on a visit to the Picture Gallery is a small room in which the chapel of the Porro di Mocchirolo oratory has been reconstructed. It now houses the frescoes that were detached from the original chapel.
This donation is of particular importance because it documents a period of great vitality in Lombard art, otherwise poorly represented in the gallery.
The style of the anonymous author of the Mocchirolo cycle displays similarities to the frescoes of other oratories in Lombardy from the second half of the fourteenth century, such as the ones at Solaro, Albizzate and Lentate. The latter, indeed, seems to have been commissioned by the same noble family, the counts of Porro.
The high quality of the painting indicates an artistic personality of the first rank, with analogies to the refined manner of Giovanni da Milano.

School of Giovanni da Milano
(second half of the 14th century)
Chapel of Santi Catarina e Ambrogio
End wall, 378x277: *Crucifixion*
Right-hand wall, 323 x 217: *Count Porro and his Family offering the Virgin a Model of the Church*
Left-hand wall, 323x217: *Saint Ambrose on his Throne scourging Two Heretics; Mystic Marriage of Saint Catherine*
Ceiling, 323x323: *The Redeemer between the Symbols of the Evangelists*
Triumphal arch, 106x61 (each): *Holy Knight* and *Christ Resurrected giving his Blessing*
Frescoes transferred onto canvas, formerly in the chapel of the Counts Porro di Mocchirolo at Lentate, Milan.

School of Giovanni da Milano, *Saint Ambrose on his Throne scourging Two Heretics.*

Facing page: View of the Mocchirolo Chapel.

Room II

This room houses a number of "gold-ground" paintings, on panel, by artists active in the fourteenth century.
The *Santa Maria della Celestia Polyptych* by Lorenzo Veneziano – whose style was certainly influenced by his contacts with Emilian painting and above all his familiarity with the work of Guariento, active in Venice over the same period – exhibits many of the most typical characteristics of its author. The painter still relied on essentially decorative criteria, as can be seen in the ornamentation of the Virgin's throne – with its openwork and many statuettes – and in the graceful gestures of the angels and the position and drapery of the saints at the sides, as well as in the sumptuous fabrics of their clothing.
A *Madonna and Child* of still uncertain date is by Ambrogio Lorenzetti, an extremely refined artist and one of the main exponents of the Sienese school of the first half of the fourteenth century. While some ascribe the picture to a fairly early period in the artist's career, others believe that it was painted when he was at the peak of his artistic maturity (1340), immediately after the frescoes in the Palazzo Pubblico of Siena.
The Florentine school is represented by Bernardo Daddi, a follower of Giotto. The Pinacoteca di Brera possesses a *Saint Lawrence* by Daddi, which is clearly the side panel of a dismembered polyptych from which the *Saint Peter* in the Courtauld Institute Galleries in London also comes.
Giovanni da Milano was active chiefly in Tuscany but originally from Lombardy. Here we can see his *Christ the Judge*, a fine example of the painter's style, in which elements of Lombard derivation are combined with the Florentine influence of Giotto.
Worth singling out, finally, as acquisitions of great interest, are the three small panels depicting *Scenes from the Life of Saint Columba*, donated to the Picture Gallery in 1960. Attributed to the eponymous Master of Saint Columba, they have recently been included in the catalogue of Giovanni Baronzio, an exponent of the school of Rimini, whose liveliness of narrative and color they reflect.

Master of Saint Veranus
(Pisa, active between ca. 1270 and 1275)
Saint Veranus between Two Angels and Six Scenes from his Legend
Tempera on panel, 152x97

Giovanni Baronzio
(Rimini, documented from 1343 to 1345)
Saint Columba before Emperor Aurelian
Saint Columba saved by a Bear
Decapitation of Saint Columba
Tempera on panel, 53x55 (each)
Compartments of altar frontal.
Donated by Anna Sessa in 1960.

Barnaba da Modena
(active between 1361 and the 1383)
Adoration of the Child
Tempera on panel, 57x50
Donated by Casimiro Sipriot in 1904.

Master of the Pesaro Crucifix
(active in Venice in the last quarter of the 14th century)
Madonna and Child and Annunciation
Tempera on panel, 68x51
Entered Brera in 1808, from the General Office of Crown Property.

Ambrose Lorenzetti
(Siena ca. 1280 – 1348?)
Madonna and Child
Tempera on panel, 85x57
Donated by Guido Cagnola in 1947.

Giovanni da Milano
(Caversaccio, Como, ca. 1320 – 1369)
Christ the Judge
Tempera on panel, 152x68
Central panel of the polyptych of Santa Maria degli Angeli in Florence.

Bernardo Daddi
(Florence ca. 1290 – 1348?)
Saint Lawrence
Tempera on panel, 43x24
Donated by Casimiro Sipriot in 1904.

Bartolomeo and Jacopino da Reggio
(active in the third quarter of the 14th century)
Crucifixion, Annunciation and Thirty Saints
Tempera on panel, 92x67 (overall)
Polyptych-reliquary. In Brera since 1889, bequest from Luciano d'Aragona.

Lorenzo Veneziano
(Venice, documented from 1356 to 1372)
Santa Maria della Celestia Polyptych
Tempera on panel
Central panel, 72x29: *Madonna and Child Enthroned with Angels*
Side panels, 31x13 (each):
bottom left: *Saints Catherine of Alexandria and Nicholas*
bottom right: *Saints Mark and Lucy*
top left: *Saints Anthony Abbot and John the Baptist*
top right: *Saints Andrew and Vittore*
Originally in the Venetian monastery of Santa Maria della Celestia and later in the Gallerie dell'Accademia at Venice, it was deposited in Brera in 1950 in exchange for Paolo Veneziano's *Coronation of the Virgin*. The fully Gothic style can be discerned in the architecture of the throne, in the gold ground against which the saints are set in graceful postures and in the richly adorned clothing.

Giovanni da Milano, *Christ the Judge.* Ambrose Lorenzetti, *Madonna and Child.*

Giovanni Baronzio, *Saint Columba saved by a Bear*, detail.

Facing page, above: Lorenzo Veneziano, *Santa Maria della Celestia Polyptych.*

Facing page, below: Giovanni Baronzio, *Saint Columba saved by a Bear* and *Decapitation of Saint Columba.*

Rooms III and IV

Italian artists who worked at the end of the fourteenth century or in the fifteenth are represented by a series of panels housed in two adjoining rooms.
The small panel depicting the *Adoration of the Magi* by Stefano da Verona (room IV), an exponent of International Gothic, is of great elegance. In this picture the taste for opulence and decoration dominates the religious element, which is subordinated to the meticulous representation of the details of the clothing and ornaments. There are also some more exotic notes, like the camel in the background or the figure of the Moor. This iconographic refinement is matched by a highly sophisticated technique, evident in the elegant use of gold paste.
Another outstanding figure in the current of International Gothic is Gentile da Fabriano. In the same room we can see his celebrated *Valle Romita Polyptych*, one of the finest paintings in the catalogue of this painter from the Marche, along with the equally famous *Adoration of the Magi* in the Galleria degli Uffizi at Florence. His works are characterized by the opulence of the costumes, the linear rhythm of the outlines and drapery and the elegant silhouettes of the figures, depicted standing on flowery swards according to the canons of International Gothic.
The late phase in the career of Jacopo Bellini, a Venetian painter considered to be the last exponent of the local Gothic tradition who was active in the fifteenth century, is exemplified by the small *Madonna and Child* (room III). In this work the artist seems to have abandoned the vestigial Gothicisms typical of the early period of his activity, gradually moving toward a representation of volumes and forms.
The Lombard painter and illuminator Bonifacio Bembo worked in the same years. He was the last representative of the late Gothic tradition in Lombardy and his works, of which the *Saint Alexis* and *Saint Julian* (room IV) are significant examples, are distinguished by their graceful and aristocratic forms and by the attention paid to the refined clothing.
Tuscan painting, which is documented in a somewhat uneven fashion at Brera, is represented in room III by a polyptych of the Sienese school painted by Andrea di Bartolo and Giorgio di Andrea, which shows the influence of the great artists Duccio di Buoninsegna and Simone Martini.

Room III

Paolo di Giovanni Fei (?)
(Siena 1346 – 1411/12)
Madonna and Child
Tempera on panel, 62·5x35

Pedro Serra
(Catalonia, documented around 1357 – 1408)
Annunciation
Tempera on panel, 59x39

Jacopo Bellini
(Venice ca. 1400 – 1470/71)
Madonna and Child
Tempera on panel, 45x50
In Brera since 1913, originally in the church of the Visitazione at Riviera di Casalfiumanese (Imola).

Giovanni da Bologna
(active at Treviso from 1377 to 1385 and at Venice in 1389)
Madonna and Child with Angels (Madonna dell'Umiltà)
Tempera on panel, 91x61
Acquired in 1910.

Nicolò di Pietro
(Venice, active from 1394 to 1430)
Coronation of the Virgin and Donors
Tempera on panel, 100x54
Donated by the Friends of Brera in 1963.

Andrea di Bartolo
(Siena 1360/65 – 1428)
and **Giorgio di Andrea**
(documented from 1410 to 1428)
Coronation of the Virgin with Saints Catherine of Alexandria, Augustine, Peter and Paul
Oil on panel, 160x65 (central panel), 142x36 (each side panel)
In Brera since 1811, it came from the convent of Santa Caterina d'Alessandria at Sant'Angelo in Vado, Urbino. This polyptych, originally set in a sumptuous frame of which only a few traces survive, was probably made up of seven panels. The two missing here are in the Galleria Nazionale delle Marche at Urbino and represent *Saint Michael Archangel* and *Saint John the Baptist.*
It was painted by Andrea di Bartolo with the assistance of his son Giorgio.

Andrea di Bartolo
The Redeemer giving his Blessing
Tempera on panel, 73x31
In Brera since 1811, originally in the church of Sant'Angelo in Vado, Urbino.

Room IV

Zavattari Workshop
(Monza, around 1440/44)
Assumption of the Virgin
Tempera on panel, 100x72·5
Donated by the heirs of Paolo Gerli in 1982.

Bonifacio Bembo
(Brescia ca. 1420 – documented until 1477)
Saint Julian
Saint Alexis

Nicolò di Pietro, *Coronation of the Virgin and Donors.*

Andrea di Bartolo and Giorgio di Andrea,
Coronation of the Virgin with Saints.

Tempera on panel, 85x28 (each)
Donated by Paolo Gerli in 1950.

Stefano da Verona
(Verona ca. 1375 – documented until 1438)
Journey and Adoration of the Magi
Tempera on panel, 72x47
Exchanged by Domenico Biasioli for two other works in 1818.

Gentile da Fabriano
(Fabriano ca. 1370 – Rome 1427)
Crucifixion
Tempera on panel, 64x40·5
Acquired in 1995.

Gentile da Fabriano
Valle Romita Polyptych
Tempera on panel
Central panel, 157x80:
Coronation of the Virgin
Lower panels, 117x40 (each):
Saints Jerome, Francis, Dominic and Mary Magdalene
Upper panels, 49x38 (each):
Torment of Saint Peter Martyr, Saint John the Baptist in the Desert, Saint Francis receiving the Stigmata, Franciscan Monk
Signed.
Originally in the church of Santa Maria di Valdisasso near Fabriano, it was dismembered and then reconstructed. Along with the *Adoration of the Magi* in the Galleria degli Uffizi at Florence, this polyptych is one of the most important of Gentile's works.

Francesco di Gentile da Fabriano
(Fabriano, active in the second half of the 15th century)
Assumption of the Virgin
Saint Sebastian between Saints Anthony Abbot and Dominic
Tempera on panel, 90x50
The panels were originally the two faces of a processional standard. In Brera since 1855, bequest from Pietro Oggioni.

Gentile da Fabriano, *Valle Romita Polyptych* and, on facing page, the central panel prior to the recent reconstruction.

Below left: Bonifacio Bembo, *Saint Julian*.

Below right: Gentile da Fabriano, *Crucifixion*.

Stefano da Verona, *Journey and Adoration of the Magi.*

Rooms V and VI

The next two rooms house representative paintings by the most important artists active in Veneto in the last decades of the fifteenth century and the early part of the sixteenth. In room V, in addition to several works that the critics ascribe to Cima da Conegliano or his workshop and a polyptych with a gold ground, a collaborative effort by Giovanni d'Alemagna and Antonio Vivarini for the abbey of Santa Maria di Praglia, near Padua, there are three panels from a predella depicting *Scenes from the Life of Saint Jerome* by Lazzaro Bastiani. A minor figure in the artistic panorama of Venice, Lazzaro Bastiani's work does show a certain liveliness of narrative that is attributed to the influence of Carpaccio.

In addition to the splendid *Saint Sebastian* by Liberale da Verona, an artist best-known for his sumptuous illuminations, such as the ones in the Choir Books of Siena Cathedral, room VI houses three canvases by Vittore Carpaccio, a painter who worked chiefly in his native city, Venice. The two canvases representing *Scenes from the Life of the Virgin*, part of the cycle from the Scuola degli Albanesi, can be dated to the first decade of the sixteenth century and are typical not only of the painter's marked tendency to create realistic settings, but also of his great narrative ability.

The Picture Gallery possesses a small but significant group of paintings by Giovanni Bellini, known as Giambellino. The most famous is undoubtedly the *Pietà*, universally recognized as one of the artist's early masterpieces. The painting stands out for its skillfully constructed composition, in which the harmonies are broken and then reestablished, as well as for the great attention paid to the humanity of the figures. The *Madonna and Child*, dated 1510, is representative instead of the last period of the Venetian painter's career, when he tended to fuse the figure and background in a harmonious way.

Andrea Mantegna, one of the most influential painters of Northern Italy in the late fifteenth century, is represented by the important *Saint Luke Polyptych*, in which critics have discerned, especially in the upper panel with the *Pietà*, the direct influence of Donatello's Paduan sculpture, certainly one of the constant references in his production. The work has affinities with the frescoes, now lost, that Mantegna painted for the Ovetari Chapel in Padua (1451), although it shows a greater mastery of the technique of perspective. Not far away hangs the *Dead Christ*, one of Mantegna's best-known works: the virtuoso use of foreshortening takes nothing away from the drama and realism of the composition. The mature phase of the Paduan artist's career is also represented by the *Madonna and Child with a Choir of Cherubim*, datable to the mid 1480s.

Room V

Lazzaro Bastiani
(Venice ca. 1425 – 1512)
Saint Jerome in the Desert
Saint Jerome bringing the Lion to the Monastery
The Death of Saint Jerome
Tempera on panel, 25x152 (overall)
Predella of the altarpiece depicting *Saint Jerome*. The main panel is still in Asolo Cathedral, the original location of the altarpiece.

Giovan Battista Cima da Conegliano
(Conegliano 1459/60 – 1517/18)
Saint Luke, the Virgin, Saint John the Baptist and Saint Mark
Saints Monica, Jerome, Nicholas and Ursula
Tempera on panel, 30x25 (each)
In Brera since 1809, originally in the church of San Giorgio Maggiore at Venice.

Girolamo da Santa Croce
(Bergamo?, active from 1503 – Venice 1556)
Saint Stephen
Oil on panel, 40x35

Master Giorgio
(Venice, active in the mid 15th century)
Saint Mark
Tempera on panel, 60x51
In Brera since 1811, originally in the Sala del Magistrato di Petizione in the Doge's Palace at Venice.

Girolamo da Treviso the Elder
(Treviso 1451 – 1497)
The Dead Christ supported by Two Angels
Oil on panel, 67x63
Acquired in 1889.

Pedro Berruguete
(Paredes de Nava, 1450/55 – Ávila ca. 1504)
Christ in Pity
Oil on panel, 71x62
In Brera since 1808.

Giovanni d'Alemagna
(Venice, documented from 1437 – Padua 1450)
and **Antonio Vivarini**
(Murano ca. 1418/20 – Venice 1476/84)
Praglia Polyptych
Oil on panel
Lower central panel, 67x33: *Madonna and Child*
Upper central panel, 47x33: *Pietà*
Lower side panels, 62x22 (each): *Saints Augustine, Benedict, John the Baptist, Jerome, Romuald (or Bernard) and Prosdocimus*
Upper side panels, 42x22 (each): *Saints Scholastica, Gregory, Peter, Paul, Ambrose and Justina*
In Brera since 1811, originally in the Benedictine abbey of Santa Maria di Praglia (Padua).

Giovan Battista Cima da Conegliano
Saint Justina
Saints Gregory and Augustine
Tempera on panel, 76x89 and 76x20
In Brera since 1811, originally in the church of Santa Giustina at Padua.

Room VI

Giovanni Martini da Udine
(Udine ca. 1470 – 1535)
Saint Ursula among her Maidens
Oil on canvas, 185x220
In Brera since 1811, originally in the church of San Pietro Martire at Udine.

Giovanni d'Alemagna and Antonio Vivarini, *Praglia Polyptych.*

Facing page: Lazzaro Bastiani, *Saint Jerome bringing the Lion to the Monastery, Saint Jerome in the Desert* and *The Death of Saint Jerome.*

Vittore Carpaccio
(Venice ca. 1455 – before 1526)
Betrothal of the Virgin
Presentation of the Virgin in the Temple
Oil on canvas, 130x140 and 130x137
In Brera since 1808, originally in the Scuola degli Albanesi at Venice.
They formed part of a cycle of six paintings by Carpaccio which, in addition to the canvases in Brera, included the *Birth, Annunciation, Visitation* and *Death of Mary*, now dispersed among different museums and collections. The two pictures in Brera are symmetrical in their composition and filled with erudite and symbolic allusions, such as the white rabbit that symbolizes the spotless fertility of Mary (*Presentation*).

Vittore Carpaccio
Disputation of Saint Stephen
Oil on canvas, 147x172
In Brera since 1808, originally in the Scuola di Santo Stefano at Venice.
Signed and dated 1514.
The painting comes from the Venetian Scuola di Santo Stefano, whose confraternity had commissioned Carpaccio to paint five pictures representing the life of St. Stephen. One of these canvases has been lost, while the others are in various museums.

Bartolomeo Montagna
(Orzinuovi, Brescia, ca. 1450 – Vicenza 1523)
Saint Jerome
Oil on panel, 51x58
Acquired in 1925.

Giovan Battista Cima da Conegliano
(Conegliano 1459/60 – 1517/18)
Saint Jerome
Oil on panel, 37x30
In Brera since 1809, originally in San Giorgio Maggiore at Venice.

Giovan Battista Cima da Conegliano
Saint Peter Enthroned with Saints John the Baptist and Paul
Oil on panel transferred onto canvas, 156x146
In Brera since 1811, originally in the Franciscan nunnery of Santa Maria Mater Domini at Conegliano.

Francesco Bissolo
(Treviso? 1470/72 – Venice 1554)
Saint Stephen with Saints Augustine and Nicholas of Tolentino
Oil on panel, 115x58 (central panel); 115x43 (each side panel)
In Brera since 1808, originally in the Scuola di Santo Stefano at Venice.

Andrea Previtali
(Berbenno, Bergamo, 1470 – Bergamo 1528)
Transfiguration (*The Redeemer*)
Oil on panel, 147·5x137·7
In Brera since 1811, originally in the church of Santa Maria delle Grazie at Bergamo.

Giovanni Bellini
(Venice 1425/30 – 1516)
Madonna and Child
Oil on panel, 85x115
Acquired in 1806 from the Ospedale Maggiore. Formerly in Palazzo Monti at Bologna.

Andrea Mantegna
(Isola di Carturo, Padua, ca. 1430 – Mantua 1506)
Saint Luke Polyptych
Tempera on panel
Central panel, 140x67: *Saint Luke*
Upper central panel, width 68: *Christ in Pity between the Madonna and Saint John*
Upper side panels, 69x40 (each): *Saints Daniel of Padua, Jerome, Maximus Bishop and Julian*
Lower side panels, 118x42 (each): *Saints Felicity, Prosdocimus, Benedict and Justina*

Giovanni Bellini
Pietà
Tempera on panel, 86x107
Donated in 1811 by Eugène de Beauharnais. Formerly in the Galleria Sampieri at Bologna.

Andrea Mantegna
Madonna and Child with a Choir of Cherubim
Tempera on panel, 88x70
In Brera since 1808, originally in Santa Maria Maggiore at Venice.

Andrea Mantegna
The Dead Christ
Tempera on canvas, 68x81
In Brera since 1824, it was formerly the property of the heirs of the painter Giuseppe Bossi.
It is not easy to reconstruct the previous history of this canvas, acquired by Giuseppe Bossi in Rome. We know that on Mantegna's death (1506), his son Ludovico sold the picture to Marchese Francesco Gonzaga to raise money to pay off his own debts; but it was Sigismondo Gonzaga who acquired it in 1507. In 1627 it was still in the Ducal Palace. With the dispersion of the Gonzaga collection and the sack of Mantua in 1630 all trace of it was lost until 1802, when it surfaced on the antiquarian market. The date of the work is extremely controversial, but recently there has been a tendency to assign it to the years 1470-74.

Giovanni Bellini
Madonna and Child (Greek Madonna)
Tempera on panel, 84x62
In Brera since 1808, originally in the Doge's Palace di Venice.
Masterpiece of the painter's early *Madonnas*, it came to Brera from the Office of the Regolatori della Scrittura in the Doge's Palace at Venice.
On the sides at the top there is an inscription in Greek letters that signifies "Mother of God" and "Christ."

Liberale da Verona
(Verona ca. 1445 – 1529/36)
Saint Sebastian
Oil on panel, 198x95
In Brera since 1811, originally in the church of San Domenico at Ancona.

Vittore Carpaccio, *Presentation of the Virgin in the Temple.*

Below: Vittore Carpaccio, *Betrothal of the Virgin.*

Vittore Carpaccio
Disputation of Saint Stephen.

Below: Bartolomeo Montagna, *Saint Jerome.*

VICTOR
CARPATHIVS
FINXIT
M
D. XIIII.

Andrea Mantegna, *Madonna and Child with a Choir of Cherubim.*

Below: Andrea Mantegna, *The Dead Christ.*

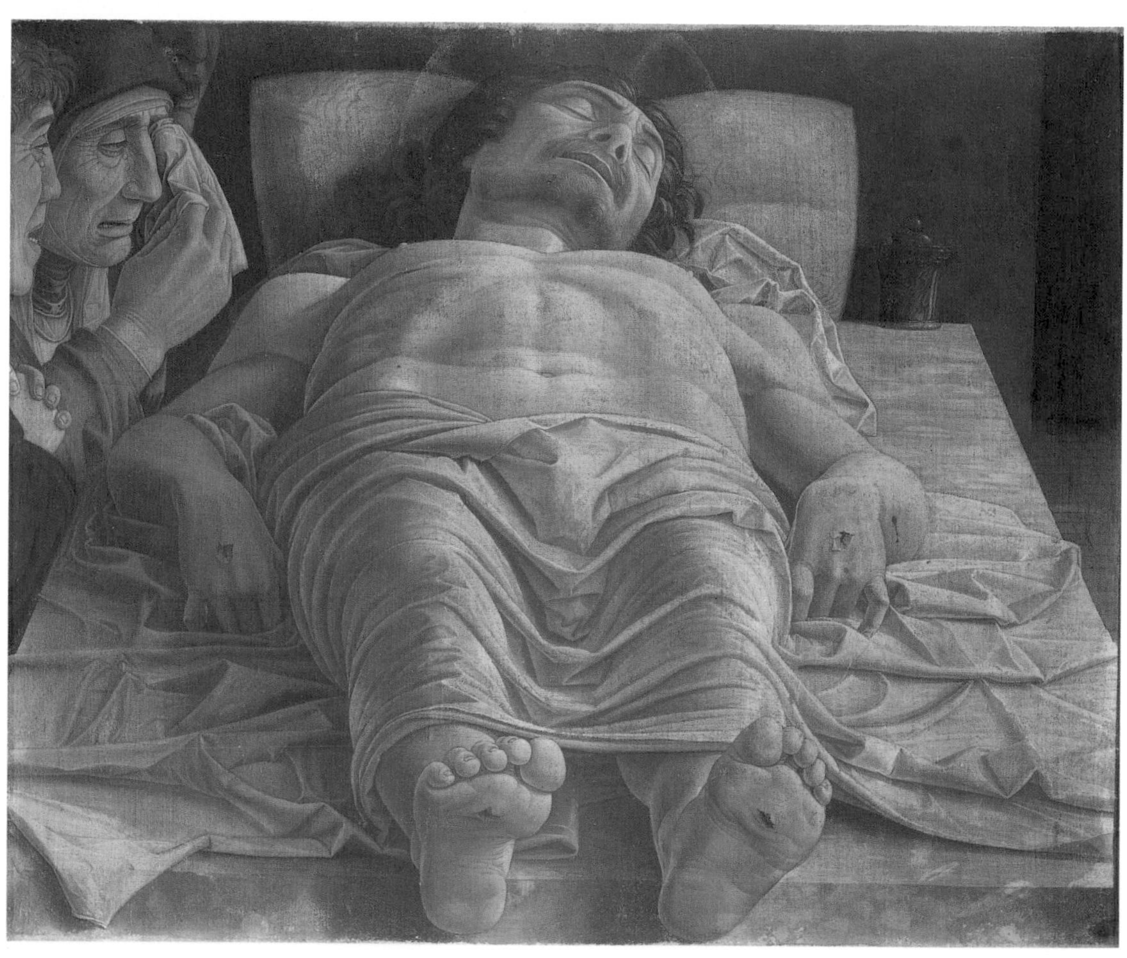

Giovanni Bellini, *Madonna and Child (Greek Madonna)*.

Below: Giovanni Bellini, *Pietà*.

Giovanni Bellini, *Madonna and Child*.

Andrea Previtali, *Transfiguration*.

Andrea Mantegna,
Saint Luke Polyptych.

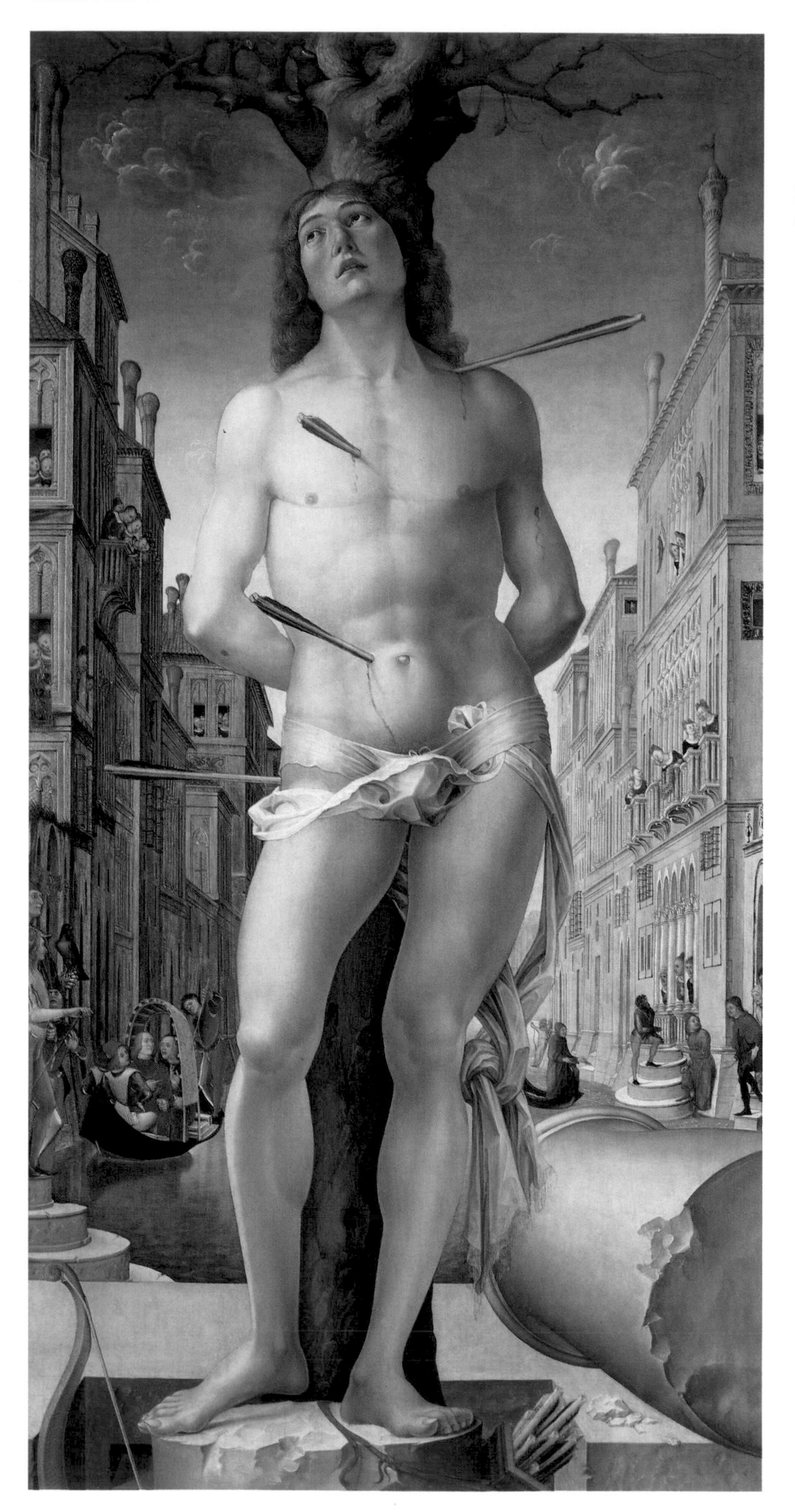

Liberale da Verona,
Saint Sebastian.

Giovan Battista Cima da Conegliano, *Saint Peter Enthroned with Saints John the Baptist and Paul.*

Room VII

Among the numerous portraits by sixteenth-century Venetian artists in this room, the *Portrait of Count Antonio di Porcia* by Tiziano Vecellio, known as Titian, is outstanding. It is a work of great naturalism in which the painter creates a sense of space by inserting a window opening onto a broad sweep of landscape in the background. He made frequent use of this device in the portraits he painted from the second decade of the sixteenth century onward, and it can be seen, for instance, in the *Baldassare Castiglione* in the National Gallery in London (1523).
The production of portraits by Lorenzo Lotto – a restless artist and great traveler whose work displays a multitude of influences – is represented by the *Portrait of an Elderly Gentleman with Gloves (Liberale da Pinedel)*. Critics regard the painting as one of the most intense works by this artist, whose style reveals a great concern for naturalism (note for example the splendid depiction of the veins in the hand) and at the same time considerable psychological insight in the representation of his subjects' expressions. There are also two pendants by Lotto, thought to be the only such pair of portraits he ever painted: they are the *Portrait of Laura da Polo* and of *Febo da Brescia*. Both signed and dating from the 1540s, they are very interesting works, notable not only for the attention paid to the character of the two sitters, but also for the depiction of the beautiful costumes which reflect the Venetian fashion of the period.
In contrast to Lotto, Paris Bordone offers a less realistic and more allusive interpretation in the *Lovers*, where the use of color is of Giorgionesque derivation.
The output of the celebrated Bergamask portraitist Giovan Battista Moroni is represented here by the intense *Antonio Navagero*, an example of the artist's "red manner" – so-called for the preponderant use of reddish tones.
In spite of the rigidity of the conventional pose, Tintoretto's *Portrait of a Young Man* is highly expressive. The work is similar to the *Portrait of an Old Man and an Adolescent* in the Kunsthistorisches Museum in Vienna and can therefore be dated to the 1560s.
Palma il Giovane's *Self-Portrait* is very interesting, even from a strictly iconographic point of view: the artist has chosen to represent himself not only with the tools of his trade, but actually in the act of painting a picture of a religious subject.

Giovanni Busi, called Cariani
(Venice ca. 1485 – ca. 1550)
Portrait of a Man
Oil on canvas, 71x57
Acquired in 1929 from the collection of Count Sottocasa in Bergamo.

Francesco Torbido, called Moro
(Venice 1480/90 – Verona ca. 1561)
Portrait of a Man
Oil on canvas, 72x56
Signed. Acquired in 1888 from the antiquarian Chiodelli of Cremona.

Tiziano Vecellio, called Titian
(Pieve di Cadore 1485/90 – Venice 1576)
Portrait of Count Antonio di Porcia
Oil on canvas, 115x90
Signed. Donated by Eugenia Litta Visconti Arese in 1891.

Lorenzo Lotto
(Venice ca. 1480 – Loreto 1556)
Portrait of a Man with Gloves (Liberale da Pinedel)
Oil on canvas, 115x98
Signed. In Brera since 1855, bequest from Pietro Oggioni.

Lorenzo Lotto
Portrait of an Elderly Gentleman with Gloves (Liberale da Pinedel)
Oil on canvas, 90x75
Signed. Acquired together with the portraits of *Laura da Pola* and *Febo da Brescia* from the Milanese antiquarian Giuseppe Baslini in 1859.

Lorenzo Lotto
Portrait of Laura da Pola
Oil on canvas, 90x75
Signed. Acquired in 1859.
This canvas, along with its pendant portraying *Febo da Brescia*, is an example of the practice of having pictures painted to celebrate a marriage, common at the time.
Lotto's register of payments records that 40 scudi were paid between September 1543 and March 1544 for the two pictures, which are apparently the only ones he ever painted as a pair.
Laura da Polo is portrayed in a rich and precious dress, testifying to her married state. In fact it was not the custom in Venice for unmarried girls to appear in public, or to dress richly.

Paris Bordone
(Treviso ca. 1500 – Venice 1571)
The Lovers
Oil on canvas, 80·5x86
Acquired from the Prinetti family of Milan in 1890.

Lorenzo Lotto
Portrait of Febo da Brescia
Oil on canvas, 82x78
Signed. In Brera since 1859.

Giovanni Battista Moroni
(Albino, Bergamo, 1520/24 – 1578)
Portrait of Antonio Navagero
Oil on canvas, 115x90
Dated. In Brera since 1813.

Giovanni Battista Moroni
Portrait of a Young Man
Oil on canvas, 56x49
In Brera since 1862 by exchange.

Jacopo Negretti, called Palma il Giovane
(Venice 1544 – 1628)
Head of Old Man (front) and *Head of Little Girl* (back)
Oil on paperboard, 38x28
In Brera since 1811, originally in the Archbishop's Palace at Milan (bequest of Cardinal Monti).

Jacopo Robusti, called Tintoretto
(Venice 1518 – 1594)
Portrait of a Young Man
Oil on canvas, 115x85
In Brera since 1857.

Palma il Giovane
Self-Portrait
Oil on canvas, 126x96
In Brera since 1811.

Titian, *Portrait of Count Antonio di Porcia.*

Above: Lorenzo Lotto, *Portrait of Laura da Pola.*

Lorenzo Lotto, *Portrait of an Elderly Gentleman with Gloves (Liberale da Pinedel).*

Above: Lorenzo Lotto, *Portrait of Febo da Brescia.*

Paris Bordone, *The Lovers.*

Palma il Giovane, *Self-Portrait*.

Room VIII

This room is dominated by the large canvas depicting *Saint Mark preaching at Alexandria*, painted by Giovanni and Gentile Bellini. Critics generally tend to make Gentile responsible for the overall layout of the composition and Giovanni for the interventions in the figures and architecture that have given the painting a more "modern" look.
Alvise Vivarini's *Assumption of the Virgin* is one of the most significant works from the early part of the career of this painter, considered to be one of the first Venetian followers of Antonello da Messina. The picture shows parallels with the panel depicting *Pentecost* in the Berlin Museums in the similarity of the figures and the disjointed drapery.
The room contains two significant compositions by Bartolomeo Montagna, who painted a fine *Saint Jerome* that is also in the gallery. The large canvas depicting the *Madonna and Child Enthroned with Saints Andrew, Monica, Ursula and Sigismund*, with its sound handling of perspective, is particularly interesting for the way in which the Venetian influences of his training are blended with his knowledge of Lombard sculpture.
The altarpieces representing the *Madonna and Child Enthroned with Members of a Confraternity* and *Saint Peter Martyr with Saints Nicholas and Benedict* are by Cima da Conegliano, a painter active in Veneto between the end of the fifteenth century and the beginning of the sixteenth. The latter, regarded as one of the painter's finest works, displays a perfect balance between the figures, the landscape in the background and the architecture, as well as the influence of Giorgione in the use of a rich and warm palette of colors.
Finally, it is worth drawing attention to the large canvas depicting the *Crucifixion* by Michele da Verona, a little-known artist who seems to have produced his best work in this picture painted (1501) for the Veronese monastery of San Giorgio in Braida.

Michele da Verona
(Verona ca. 1470 – 1536/44)
Crucifixion
Oil on canvas, 335x720
Signed and dated 1501.

Giovan Battista Cima da Conegliano
(Conegliano 1459/60 – 1517/18)
Saint Peter Martyr with Saints Nicholas and Benedict
Oil on panel transferred onto canvas, 330x216
In Brera since 1811.
This large picture, perhaps one of the most important of Cima da Conegliano's works, came from the monastery of Corpus Domini in Venice, where it had been commissioned by the spice merchant Benedetto Carlone as an altarpiece for his own mortuary chapel. The picture was painted between 1505 and 1506.

Gentile Bellini
(Venice 1429 – 1507)
and **Giovanni Bellini**
(Venice 1425/30 – 1516)
Saint Mark preaching in Alexandria
Oil on canvas, 347x770
In Brera since 1809.
Commissioned from Gentile in 1504 by the Scuola Grande di San Marco, the picture was left unfinished at the time of his death (1507). Gentile left precise instructions in his will that it should be finished by his brother Giovanni.

Giovan Battista Cima da Conegliano
Madonna and Child Enthroned with Saints Sebastian, John the Baptist, Mary Magdalene and Rock and Kneeling Members of the Confraternity
Tempera on panel transferred onto canvas, 301x211
In Brera since 1811, originally in the Scuola di San Giovanni Battista at Oderzo.

Giovanni Mansueti
(Venice ca. 1465/70 – 1526/7)
Saint Mark baptizing Saint Anianus
Oil on canvas, 335x135
Signed. In Brera since 1808, originally in the Scuola Grande di San Marco at Venice.

Alvise Vivarini
(Venice ca. 1450 – 1505)
Assumption of the Virgin
Mixed tempera on panel, 225x114
In Brera since 1811, originally in the Franciscan church of the Incoronata at Martinengo (Brescia).

Marcello Fogolino
(Vicenza ca. 1475 – Trent? after 1548)
Madonna and Child Enthroned and Saints Job and Gothard
Oil on panel, 203x160
In Brera since 1812, originally in the church of San Biagio at Vicenza.

Francesco Bonsignori
(Verona ca. 1460 – Caldiero, Verona, 1519)
Saints Louis and Bernardine (or Francis?) holding the Monogram of Christ
Oil on canvas, 110x170
In Brera since 1811, originally in the church of San Francesco at Mantua.

Jacopo Negretti, called Palma il Vecchio
(Serina, Bergamo, ca. 1480 – Venice 1528)
Constantine and Saint Helen between Saints Sebastian and Rock
Oil on panel, 163x84 (central panel), 143x61 (each side panel)
In Brera since 1804. Donated by Francesco Melzi.

Bartolomeo Montagna
(Orzinuovi, Brescia, ca. 1450 – Vicenza 1523)
Madonna and Child Enthroned between Saints Francis and Bernardine
Panel, 215x166

Bartolomeo Montagna
Madonna and Child Enthroned with Saints Andrew, Monica, Ursula and Sigismund and Angels playing Music
Oil on canvas, 410x260
In Brera since 1811, originally in the Squarzi Chapel of the church of San Michele at Vicenza.

Andrea Mantegna
(Isola di Carturo, Padua, ca. 1430 – Mantua 1506)
and assistants
Saint Bernardine of Siena and Angels
Tempera on canvas, 385x220
Dated 1469. In Brera since 1811, originally on the altar of the chapel of San Bernardino in the church of San Francesco at Mantua.

Francesco Morone
(Verona ca. 1471 – 1529)
Madonna and Child Enthroned between Saints Zeno and Nicholas
Tempera on canvas, 192x125
Signed, date not legible (1503?). In Brera since 1811, originally on the altar of San Zeno in the church of San Giacomo alla Pigna at Verona.

Giovan Battista Cima da Conegliano, *Saint Peter Martyr with Saints Nicholas and Benedict.*

D·G·I· P·N·O
M D
OPVS
BARTHOLOMEI
MONTA
GNA

Facing page: Bartolomeo Montagna, *Madonna and Child Enthroned with Saints and Angels playing Music.*

Michele da Verona, *Crucifixion.*

Above: Gentile and Giovanni Bellini, *Saint Mark preaching in Alexandria.*

Gentile and Giovanni Bellini, *Saint Mark preaching in Alexandria*, details.

Room IX

In this room we find paintings by some of the most important Venetian artists of the sixteenth century. The Venetian painting of that period is exemplified by the four canvases by Jacopo Tintoretto, which can be said to represent some of the salient phases in his activity.
The *Allegory of Fortune*, still characterized by accentuated plastic effects and twisted and difficult poses, is from the early part of the career of this painter, traditionally considered a pupil of Titian but in reality influenced by the Tusco-Roman and Emilian styles. The canvas depicting *Saints Helen, Barbara, Andrew and Macarius, another Saint and a Devotee* has echoes of the work of Veronese and is typical of a more mature phase.
On the other hand, the *Finding of Saint Mark's Remains*, one of the Venetian master's most celebrated and fascinating works, testifies to Tintoretto's interest in the spatial dynamics of the composition, as well as to his tendency to construct forms by means of light, which is treated as a dramatic element.
The fundamental elements in the pictorial style of another great Venetian artist, Paolo Caliari, called Veronese, are the tendency to use large areas of color steeped in a generally pale and soft light and a predisposition to frame the composition in complex architectural sets. This can be seen in the imposing canvas depicting the *Supper in the House of Simon*, one of the painter's favorite subjects, whose splendid and vivid tones allow us to fully appreciate his mastery of color.
Another picture rich in color and filled with light, the canvas with the *Baptism and Temptations of Christ*, hanging on the opposite side of the room, also reveals Veronese's great skill as a landscape painter. He made particularly effective use of this ability in his great decorative cycles of frescoes.
The third great exponent of sixteenth-century Venetian painting, Titian, is represented by the *Penitent Saint Jerome*. A dramatic and intense work, rich in warm tones, it is typical of the mature phase of the artist's career, in which the critics discern a reemergence of Mannerist ideas and an attempt to make the figures blend in with the surrounding landscape.

Lorenzo Lotto
(Venice ca. 1480 – Loreto 1556)
Pietà
Oil on canvas, 185x150
Signed. In Brera since 1811, originally in the church of San Paolo at Treviso.

Tiziano Vecellio, called Titian
(Pieve di Cadore 1485/90 – Venice 1576)
Penitent Saint Jerome
Oil on panel, 235x125
Signed. In Brera since 1808, originally in the church of Santa Maria Nuova at Venice.

Paolo Caliari, called Veronese
(Verona 1528 – Venice 1588)
Last Supper
Oil on canvas, 220x523
In Brera since 1811, originally in the church of Santa Sofia at Venice.

Paolo Veronese
Baptism and Temptations of Christ
Oil on canvas, 248x450
In Brera since 1809, originally in the church of San Nicolò ai Frari at Venice.

Alessandro Varotari, called Padovanino (Padua 1588 - Venice 1649)
The Victory of the Carnutes over the Normans
Oil on canvas, 510x587.
Signed and dated 1618.
From the church of Santa Maria Maggiore in Venice.

Jacopo Robusti, called Tintoretto
(Venice 1518 – 1594)
The Miracle of Saint Mark (Finding of Saint Mark's Remains)
Oil on canvas, 400x400
In Brera since 1811.
It belongs to a cycle of paintings representing scenes from the saint's life that used to hang on the walls of the Scuola Grande di San Marco. The dates assigned to the canvas range from 1562 to 1566, when the *guardian grande* of the Scuola, the physician Tommaso Rangone, obtained permission to pay for it himself. The knight kneeling in the background, is a portrait of the donor.

Tintoretto
Saints Helen, Barbara, Andrew and Macarius, another Saint and a Devotee worshipping the Cross
Oil on canvas, 275x165
In Brera since 1805, originally in the church of Santa Croce at Milan.

Tintoretto
Allegory of Fortune
Oil on canvas, 96x140
In Brera since 1808.

Tintoretto
Pietà
Oil on canvas, 108x170
In Brera since 1808, originally in the Procuratie di San Marco at Venice.

Paolo Veronese
Saint Anthony Abbot between Saints Cornelius and Cyprian
Oil on canvas, 270x180
In Brera since 1808, originally in the church of Sant'Antonio Abate on Torcello.

Paolo Veronese
Supper in the House of Simon
Oil on canvas, 275x710
In Brera since 1816.
The picture was painted in 1570 for the refectory of the Venetian monastery of San Sebastiano. It forms part of a series of pictures of banquets that begins with the *Wedding Feast at Cana* (Paris, Louvre).

Paolo Veronese
Christ in the Garden of Gethsemane
Oil on canvas, 108x180
In Brera since 1808, formerly in the church of Santa Maria Maggiore at Venice.

Jacopo da Ponte, called Jacopo Bassano
(Bassano ca. 1510 – 1592)
Saint Rock visiting Plague Victims
Oil on canvas, 350x210
Signed. In Brera since 1811, originally in the church of San Rocco at Vicenza.

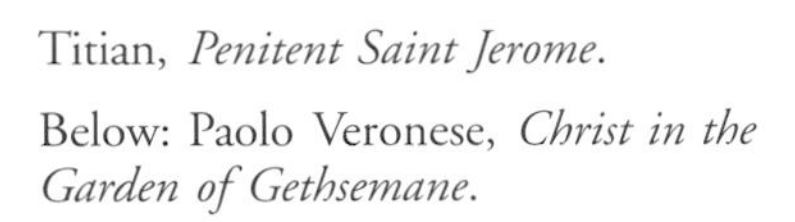

Titian, *Penitent Saint Jerome*.

Below: Paolo Veronese, *Christ in the Garden of Gethsemane*.

Paolo Veronese, *Supper in the House of Simon.*

Paolo Veronese, *Baptism and Temptations of Christ*.

Above: Paolo Veronese, *Last Supper*.

Tintoretto, *The Miracle of Saint Mark.*

Tintoretto, *Saints Helen, Barbara, Andrew and Macarius, another Saint and a Devotee worshipping the Cross.*

Facing page: Giovanni Battista Moroni, *Assumption of the Virgin.*

Room XIV

Further examples of the Pinacoteca di Brera's rich collection of Venetian painting can be seen in this room, which houses works by painters active in the sixteenth century, some of them originally from eastern Lombardy, an area whose art was strongly influenced by Veneto. They include the Brescian Gerolamo Romanino, who is represented by the *Madonna and Child*, painted around the second decade of the sixteenth century – on the artist's return from a stay in Padua where he would have been able to see Titian's frescoes for himself – and the later *Presentation in the Temple* (1529), influenced by the young Moretto, with whom he had worked on the chapel of the Sacrament in San Giovanni Evangelista at Brescia. There are three works by Alessandro Bonvicino, called Moretto, another painter from Brescia. They include panels from a dismembered polyptych originally in the Val Trompia and a small *Madonna and Child*, dating from between the fourth and fifth decade of the century, which is one of the best half-length compositions he ever painted. We can also admire two pictures of sacred subjects by his faithful pupil Giovanni Battista Moroni – famous for his portraits – in which the reference to his master's compositions is still strong. The *Madonna and Child Enthroned with Angels between Saints* by the Bergamask Giovanni Busi, called Cariani, is typical of the mature phase of the artist's career, when he came under the sway of Giorgione's naturalism and the coloration of Titian's late works, as well as the style of Lorenzo Lotto. The room also houses a large altarpiece depicting the *Madonna and Child with Saints* (1524-25) by Gerolamo Savoldo, one of the most refined of Brescian colorists who liked to use grazing light to create virtuoso shimmering effects on the fabrics of the clothing.
Other artists active in Venice were the Dutchman Lambert Sustris, who painted the small picture of the *Road to Calvary*, and the Veronese Bonifacio de' Pitati. The canvas representing *Moses saved from the Waters* is one of the finest works by this artist, who manages to bring out the narrative dimension of the sacred event while using a palette that once again recalls Giorgione's mastery of color.

Giovanni Antonio de' Sacchis, called Pordenone
(Pordenone 1483/84 – Ferrara 1539)
Transfiguration
Tempera on panel, 93x64
Entered Brera by confiscation in 1925/26. Formerly in the castle of San Salvatore at Collalto, Treviso.

Gerolamo Romani, called Romanino
(Brescia 1484/87 – 1560)
Madonna and Child
Oil on panel, 83x62
In Brera since 1896, originally in the Archbishop's Palace at Milan (bequest of Cardinal Monti).

Lorenzo Lotto
(Venice ca. 1480 – Loreto 1556)
Assumption of the Virgin
Oil on panel, 27x56
Predella of the *Recanati Transfiguration.*
In Brera since 1855, bequest from Pietro Oggioni. Formerly in the Mattei collection at Rome.

Alessandro Bonvicino, called Moretto
(Brescia 1497/98 – 1552)
Madonna and Child
Oil on canvas, 49x57
Acquired in 1911. Formerly in the Gustavo Frizzoni collection.

Moretto
Our Lady of the Assumption between Saints Jerome, Mark (?), Catherine of Alexandria, Clare and Francis of Assisi
Oil on panel, 148x60 (central panel), 103x30 and 114x60 (side panels)
Parts of a dismembered polyptych. In Brera since 1808, originally in the church of Santa Maria degli Angeli at Gardone Val Trompia.

Moretto
Madonna and Child in Glory and Saints Jerome, Francis and Anthony Abbot
Oil on canvas, 255x185
In Brera since 1808, originally in the church of Santa Maria degli Angeli at Gardone Val Trompia.

Giovanni Battista Moroni
(Albino, Bergamo, 1520/24 – 1578)
Madonna and Child with Saints Catherine and Francis and the Donor
Oil on canvas, 102x110
Entered Brera in 1818 by exchange with Giuseppe Chinetti.

Giovanni Gerolamo Savoldo
(Brescia? ca. 1480 – Venice? after 1548)
Madonna in Glory and Child, Angels and Saints Peter, Dominic, Paul and Jerome
Oil on panel, 475x307
Signed. In Brera since 1811. Commissioned by Dominican monks for the high altar of the church of San Domenico in Pesaro, it was painted in 1524-25. Note the marvelous view in the background, which is reminiscent of the Fondamenta Nuove in Venice. The painter's signature is set on the stone on which St. Jerome has placed his foot.

Romanino
Presentation of Jesus in the Temple
Oil on panel, 188x140
Signed and dated 1529. Acquired in 1923.

Giovanni Battista Moroni
Assumption of the Virgin
Oil on canvas, 330x225
Signed. In Brera since 1811, originally in the church of San Benedetto at Bergamo.

Giovanni Busi, called Cariani
(Bergamo ca. 1480 – Venice 1547)
Madonna and Child Enthroned with Angels between Saints Apollonia, Augustine, Catherine, Joseph, Grata, Philip Benizzi and Barbara
Oil on canvas, 270x211
In Brera since 1805, originally in the church of San Gottardo at Bergamo.

Cariani
Resurrection of Christ between Saints Jerome and John the Baptist and the Donors Ottaviano and Domitilla Vimercati
Oil on canvas, 208x170
Donated by Paolo Gerli in 1957.

Bonifacio de' Pitati
(Verona ca. 1487 – Venice 1553)
Christ and the Woman taken in Adultery
Oil on canvas, 175x340
In Brera since 1811, originally in the Archbishop's Palace at Milan (bequest of Cardinal Monti).

Bonifacio de' Pitati
Moses saved from the Waters
Oil on canvas, 175x345
In Brera since 1811, originally in the Archbishop's Palace at Milan (bequest of Cardinal Monti).

Lambert Sustris
(Amsterdam 1515/20 – Venice ca. 1584)
Road to Calvary
Oil on canvas, 106x131
In Brera since 1855, bequest from Pietro Oggioni.

Paris Bordone
(Treviso ca. 1500 – Venice 1571)
The Baptism of Jesus
Oil on canvas, 175x202
In Brera since 1811, originally in the Archbishop's Palace at Milan (bequest of Cardinal Monti).

Paris Bordone
The Virgin commending Saint Dominic to the Redeemer
Oil on panel, 148x106
Signed. In Brera since 1811, originally in the church of San Paolo at Treviso.

Paris Bordone
Holy Family and Saint Ambrose presenting a Donor
Oil on panel, 93x130
In Brera since 1896, originally in the Archbishop's Palace at Milan.

Paris Bordone
Pentecost
Oil on canvas, 305x220
In Brera since 1811, originally in the church of the Spirito Santo at Crema.

Jacopo Negretti, called Palma il Vecchio
(Serina, Bergamo, 1480 – Venice 1528)
Adoration of the Magi in the Presence of Saint Helen
Oil on canvas, 470x260
In Brera since 1811, originally in the church of Sant'Elena in Isola at Venice.

Facing page: Moretto, *Madonna and Child*.

Cariani, *Madonna and Child Enthroned with Angels and Saints*.

Bonifacio de' Pitati, *Moses saved from the Waters.*

Romanino, *Presentation of Jesus in the Temple.*

Room XV

This room contains paintings, mostly of a large size, by artists who worked in Lombardy during the fifteenth and sixteenth centuries. On the wall opposite the entrance, we can see several works by one of the founders of the Lombard school of painting, Vincenzo Foppa, an artist of Brescian origin. The polyptych from the Bergamask church of Santa Maria delle Grazie, datable to the early 1480s, has the typical Renaissance layout of a number of compartments, with the saints enclosed in a mock portico. The beautiful glimpses of landscape visible in the background of each compartment are also characteristic of Foppa's art. The *Madonna and Child* and *Martyrdom of Saint Sebastian*, on the other hand, are frescoes detached from the destroyed church of Santa Maria di Brera in Milan, and clearly show the artist's application of the rules of perspective derived from Bramante's prototypes.

The *Madonna Enthroned and Child, the Doctors of the Church and the Family of Ludovico il Moro* by the anonymous Master of the Sforza Altarpiece is a rather interesting work. It was commissioned by Ludovico il Moro (who is portrayed kneeling along with his consort Beatrice d'Este) for the Milanese church of Sant'Ambrogio ad Nemus (1494) and bears witness to the taste of the Sforza court for magnificence and self-celebration.

Here we see three very fine paintings by Bartolomeo Suardi, called Bramantino. They include the *Crucifixion*, regarded by critics as a work at once tragic and classical, which displays some of the characteristics of his late phase, such as the classicism of the forms and his fondness for ample drapery and monumental architectural backdrops, and the contemporary *Madonna and Child.*

If Bramantino's painting constitutes an intelligent and original alternative to the "Leonardism" that dominated Lombard culture at the beginning of the century, the output of Marco d'Oggiono, who was Leonardo's pupil, lies wholly under the shadow of his master, as is apparent from the large altarpiece representing the *Three Archangels*, painted for the church of Santa Marta at Milan.

An artist of Piedmontese origin, but active in the Lombard region as well, was Gaudenzio Ferrari. There are numerous works by him in this room, including the detached frescoes from the Milanese church of Santa Maria della Pace which reveal the painter's gift for narrative, and the complex panel depicting the *Martyrdom of Saint Catherine of Alexandria*, with its almost theatrical style.

Gaudenzio Ferrari
(Valduggia, Vercelli, 1475 – Milan 1546)
Presentation of Mary in the Temple, 186 x 65
The Moorish King, 190x65
Adoration of the Magi, 190x136
Procession of the Magi, 190x65
Assumption of the Virgin, 105x105
Angels playing Music, 105x105
In Brera since 1808. Frescoes transferred onto canvas, formerly in the chapel of the Nativity of the Virgin in Santa Maria della Pace at Milan.
The Franciscans, to whom the church of Santa Maria della Pace belonged, were important patrons in Lombardy around the end of the fifteenth century and the beginning of the sixteenth. They had, for example, already commissioned from Gaudenzio *The Martyrdom of Saint Catherine* for the church of Sant'Angelo and, from Luini, the decoration of the chapel of San Giuseppe in the same church of Santa Maria della Pace. The preferred themes of this religious order were the birth and early years of Mary and the cult of Ann and Joachim which seems to have been spread by the Franciscans themselves in the late Middle Ages.

Gaudenzio Ferrari
Martyrdom of Saint Catherine of Alexandria
Oil on panel, 334x210
Acquired in 1829. Formerly in the church of Sant'Angelo at Milan.

Gaudenzio Ferrari
Madonna and Child
Oil on panel, 100x75
Perhaps part of a polyptych formerly in the chapel of Santa Margherita di Varallo. In Brera since 1890, originally in the Prinetti collection at Milan.

Bartolomeo Suardi, called Bramantino
(Milan ca. 1465 – 1530)
Madonna and Child
Oil on panel, 61x47
In Brera since 1896, originally in the Archbishop's Palace at Milan (bequest of Cardinal Cesare Monti).
This is considered to be a significant and important work from Bramantino's late maturity, perhaps dating from 1510-13. The identity of the figure seen almost in profile on the left of the picture is disputed, but is probably St. Joseph, while the two small figures in the background may represent the meeting of Ann and Joachim.

Bramantino
Madonna and Child with Angels
Detached fresco, 240x135
In Brera since 1808, originally in the Palazzo della Ragione at Milan.

Bramantino
Crucifixion
Oil on canvas, 372x270
In Brera since 1806.
We do not know the original location of this canvas which, previously attributed to Bramante and regarded as not very successful in its handling of the proportions and drapery, was removed from Brera (1841-61). Later it was returned to the gallery, but without being put on display. In 1871 Cavalcaselle assigned it to Bramantino and since then it has become one of the most famous works in the Pinacoteca di Brera.

Vincenzo Foppa
(Brescia ca. 1427 – ca. 1515)
Martyrdom of Saint Sebastian
Fresco detached and transferred onto canvas, 265x170
In Brera since 1808, originally in the church of Santa Maria di Brera.

Vincenzo Foppa
Madonna and Child with Saints John the Baptist and

Master of the Sforza Altarpiece, *Madonna Enthroned and Child, the Doctors of the Church and the Family of Lodovico il Moro.*

John the Evangelist
Fresco detached and transferred onto canvas, 192x173
Dated 1485. In Brera since 1808, originally in the church of Santa Maria di Brera.

Vincenzo Foppa
Santa Maria delle Grazie Polyptych
Tempera and oil on panel
Lower central panel, 185x98: *Madonna and Child with Angels*
Upper central panel, 144x96: *Saint Francis receiving the Stigmata*
Top, 42x41: *Christ giving his Blessing*
Lower side panels, 150x96 (each): *Saints Jerome and Alexander, Vincent and Anthony of Padua*
Upper side panels, 140x98 (each): *Saints Clare and Bonaventure, Louis of Toulouse and Bernardine of Siena*
Predella, 42x97: *Annunciation, Visitation, Two Angels with the Emblem of the Passion, the Nativity* and *Flight into Egypt*
Originally in the church of Santa Maria delle Grazie at Bergamo. Reassembled in 1912.
The polyptych arrived in Brera in a damaged state, with part of the frame missing, as it had been dismembered for easier sale on the antiquarian market. The five small panels of the predella were acquired later (1912).
In the past the complexity of the composition has prompted many doubts over the attribution and history of the work. It is now believed to have been painted around 1483. The dais on which Mary's throne stands bears a striking resemblance to the apses of Bramante's church of Santa Maria delle Grazie in Milan.

Master of the Sforza Altarpiece
(Lombardy, ca. 1490 – ca. 1520)
Madonna Enthroned and Child, the Doctors of the Church and the Family of Lodovico il Moro
Tempera on panel, 230x165
In Brera since 1808, originally in the church of Sant'Ambrogio ad Nemus at Milan.

Giovanni Bernardino and **Giovan Stefano Scotti**
(Lombardy, documented from 1485 to 1520)
Crucifixion with Saints Catherine, Francis, Bonaventure (?) and Peter
Oil on panel, 243x143
In Brera since 1905, formerly in the church of Sant'Angelo at Milan.

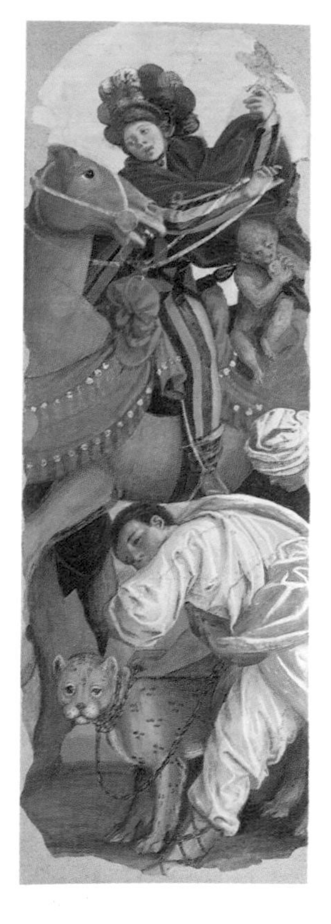

Gaudenzio Ferrari, *Procession of the Magi*, *Adoration of the Magi* and *The Moorish King*.

Ambrose da Fossano, called Bergognone
(Milan ca. 1453 – 1523)
Assumption of the Virgin and Saints and *Coronation of the Virgin* (lunette)
Oil on panel, 271x245 and 125x245
Signed and dated 1522.
In Brera since 1809, originally in the church of Santa Maria Incoronata at Nerviano (Milan).

Bernardino Luini (?)
(Milan 1480/90 – 1532)
Annunciation
Oil on panel, 265x165
In Brera since 1805, originally in the church of Santa Marta at Milan.

Marco d'Oggiono
(Oggiono, Como, 1475 – Milan ca. 1530)
The Elevation of the Magdalen
Oil on panel, 146x103
In Brera since 1989, recovered in Germany through the Bonn accord.

Marco d'Oggiono
The Three Archangels
Oil on panel, 255x190
Signed. In Brera since 1808, originally in the church of Santa Marta at Milan.

Gaudenzio Ferrari
Scenes from the Story of Joachim and Ann
Frescoes transferred onto canvas
Lower central panel, 190x135: *Announcement of the Birth of Mary*
Upper central tondo, diameter 115: *Consecration of Mary*
Lower side panels, 190x65 (each): *Lament of Ann* and *Expulsion of Joachim from the Temple*
Upper side panels, 105x105 (each): *Announcing Angel* and *Virgin Mary*

Marco d'Oggiono, *The Three Archangels.*

Facing page: Gaudenzio Ferrari, *Martyrdom of Saint Catherine of Alexandria.*

Bramantino, *Madonna and Child.*

Bramantino, *Crucifixion*.

Vincenzo Foppa, *Santa Maria delle Grazie Polyptych*.

Facing page: Vincenzo Foppa, *Martyrdom of Saint Sebastian*.

Room XVIII

During the sixteenth century many artists of Cremonese origin played an important role in the world of Lombard painting, often working in Milan as well. Among those active in the fifteenth and sixteenth century were Boccaccio Boccaccino, who painted the small *Madonna and Child* we see here, and Altobello Melone, represented by two pictures, one of them a *Portrait of Alda Gambara* with an interesting view of Brescia Castle in the background.
One of the families of painters that dominated the artistic scene in Cremona over the course of the sixteenth century was that of the Campi brothers. Brera possesses a *Madonna and Child with Saints* by Giulio Campi, the oldest of the three, which shows the marked influence of the Emilian followers of Raphael as well as coloristic elements derived from Romanino. Antonio Campi is represented by a *Madonna and Child with Saints Joseph, Catherine and Agnes*, a work of great refinement and elegance, while the style of the youngest of the brothers, Vincenzo, is documented by two canvases with genre scenes. It was mainly toward the end of his career that Vincenzo devoted himself to this type of painting: in fact a number of examples are known which reveal the influence of Flemish artists, and yet display an essentially Lombard vein, to the point where his still-life compositions have often been seen as the true forerunners of Caravaggio's work.
Bernardino Campi – another painter from Cremona and the author of an elegant *Dead Christ* on show here – was the teacher of Sofonisba Anguissola, a refined woman painter who was highly esteemed in her day. She also specialized in portraiture, well-exemplified here by the small *Portrait of Minerva Anguissola (Self-Portrait?)*. Another significant female portrait painter was Lavinia Fontana from Bologna, whose *Family Portrait* is in Brera.
The Piazza family was originally from Lodi. It is represented here by a picture of *Saint John the Baptist* by Martino and three works by his son Callisto, including an imposing *Baptism of Christ*, which was undoubtedly inspired by Gaudenzio Ferrari's altarpiece depicting a similar subject in Santa Maria presso San Celso at Milan.
The Lombard painting of the end of the sixteenth century is represented by Giovanni Ambrogio Figino (*Portrait of Lucio Foppa*) and Giovanni Paolo Lomazzo, a treatise writer and theorist on Milanese art whose *Self-Portrait*, painted (1568) just a few years before he went blind, reveals the persistence of Leonardo's influence, enlivened by Northern European elements.

Martino Piazza
(Lodi 1475/80 – ca. 1523)
Saint John the Baptist
Oil on panel, 183x57
In Brera since 1805.

Lombard painter
(active at the beginning of the 16th century)
Madonna and Child between Saints Paul and John the Baptist
Oil on panel, 228x150
In Brera since 1808, originally in the church (no longer in existence) of San Paolo in Compito at Milan.

Giovanni Agostino da Lodi, formerly Pseudo Boccaccino
(Lombardy, active from the last decade of the 15th century until ca. 1520)
Madonna and Child with an Angel
Oil on panel, 75x67
Acquired in 1912 by Teresa Ciceri of Como.

Callisto Piazza
(Lodi ca. 1500 – 1562)
Mystic Marriage of Saint Catherine
Oil on panel, 38x51
Acquired in 1935.

Callisto Piazza
The Baptism of Jesus
Oil on canvas, 295x255
In Brera since 1811, originally in the church of Santa Catherine at Crema.

Altobello Melone
(Cremona ca. 1485 – before 1543)
Portrait of Alda Gambara
Oil on panel, 60x50

Vincenzo Campi
(Cremona 1536 – 1591)
The Fruit Seller
Oil on canvas, 144x217
In Brera since 1809.

Vincenzo Campi
The Fishmonger
Oil on canvas, 143x213
In Brera since 1809.

Sofonisba Anguissola
(Cremona 1527 – Palermo 1625)
Portrait of Minerva Anguissola (Self-Portrait?)
Oil on canvas, 36x29
Signed. Acquired in 1911 from the antiquarian Carlo Zen.

Lavinia Fontana
(Bologna 1552 – Rome 1614)
Family Portrait
Oil on canvas, 105x85
In Brera since 1808, originally in the Milanese seat of the Ministry of Finance.

Giovanni Ambrose Figino
(Milan ca. 1551/54 – 1608)
Portrait of Lucio Foppa
Oil on panel, 180x100
Signed. In Brera since 1809, originally in the Sannazzari collection, donated to the Ospedale Maggiore in 1802.

Giovan Paolo Lomazzo
(Milan 1538 – 1600)
Self-Portrait
Oil on canvas, 56x44
In Brera since 1821 by exchange.

Antonio Campi
(Cremona 1523 – 1587)
Portrait of Bartolomeo Arese
Oil on panel, 56x49
Ceded by the Radlinsky family of Milan in 1962.

Giovan Paolo Lomazzo
The Crucifixion, the Virgin, Saint John and the Magdalen
Oil on panel, 250x148
In Brera since 1809, originally in San Giovanni in Conca at Milan.

Giovanni Ambrose Figino
Madonna and Child with Saints John the Evangelist and Michael
Oil on canvas, 314x175
In Brera since 1805, originally in the chapel of San Giovanni Evangelista in the Collegio dei Dottori (Palazzo dei Giureconsulti) at Milan.

Bernardino Campi
(Cremona 1522 – 1591)

The Dead Christ
Oil on canvas, 235x165
Signed and dated 1574.
In Brera since 1811.

Sofonisba Anguissola
Pietà
Oil on panel, 44x27
Acquired in 1909.

Antonio Campi
Madonna and Child with Saints Joseph, Catherine and Agnes
Oil on canvas, 230x145
Signed. In Brera since 1810, originally in the church of San Barnaba at Milan.

Camillo Boccaccino
(Cremona ca. 1505 – 1546)
Madonna and Child with Saints
Oil on canvas, 296x165
Signed and dated 1532.
In Brera since 1809, originally in the church of San Bartolomeo at Cremona.

Giulio Campi
(Cremona ca. 1508 – 1573)
Madonna and Child with Saints Catherine of Alexandria and Francis and the Donor Stampa Soncino
Oil on panel, 266x167
Signed and dated 1530.
In Brera since 1883, originally in the church of Santa Maria delle Grazie at Soncino.

Callisto Piazza
Madonna and Child with Saints John the Baptist and Jerome
Oil and tempera on panel, 215x188
Signed. Acquired in 1829 from the Counts Lechi of Brescia.

Altobello Melone
Deposition of Christ
Oil on panel, 160x175
Acquired in 1916 from the Pio Ricovero di Maternità in Milan.

Boccaccio Boccaccino
(Cremona ca. 1465 – 1524/25)
Madonna and Child playing with a Little Bird
Oil on panel, 49x40
Acquired in 1925.

Gian Pietro Rizzi, called Giampietrino
(Milan, documented in the first half of the 16th century)
Madonna and Child
Oil on panel, 49x38
Acquired in 1995.

Sofonisba Anguissola, *Portrait of Minerva Anguissola (Self-Portrait?)*.

Above:
Lavinia Fontana, *Family Portrait*.

Antonio Campi, *Madonna and Child with Saints Joseph, Catherine and Agnes.*

Facing page, above: Vincenzo Campi, *The Fruit Seller.*

Facing page, below: Vincenzo Campi, *The Fishmonger.*

Giovanni Ambrose Figino, *Portrait of Lucio Foppa.*
Above left: Altobello Melone, *Portrait of Alda Gambara.*
Alongside: Giovan Paolo Lomazzo, *Self-Portrait.*

Room XIX

The "Leonardesque" artists – and the term covers both the pupils of Leonardo da Vinci and those painters active at the end of the fifteenth century and the beginning of the sixteenth century who were influenced in some way by the art of the great Tuscan master – are represented in this room by a number of pictures of small size, very often intended for private devotion, in contrast to the ones in room XV which mostly come from religious buildings.
In addition to two beautiful portraits by Giovanni Antonio Boltraffio (*Portrait of Gerolamo Casio*) and Andrea Solario (*Portrait of a Young Man*), late fifteenth-century Lombard portraiture is exemplified here by Giovanni Ambrogio De Predis's *Portrait of a Young Man*, a picture of great psychological penetration and characteristic of the painter's main field of interest.
Cesare da Sesto's *Madonna dell'Albero* reflects a particular moment in the artist's career, in which he blended elements derived from Leonardo with ideas drawn from Raphaelesque classicism.
Bernardino Luini, one of the most sensitive and measured interpreters of "Leonardism," is represented here by the *Madonna del Roseto*, which can be linked with many of Leonardo's own drawings. It is a work of high quality that immediately found favor with his contemporaries and displays affinities with the master in the use of chiaroscuro and the delicacy of the flesh tones.
An artist who did not belong to the school of Leonardo, but was representative instead of a still fully fifteenth-century culture, is Bergognone. Here we can see his *Madonna and Child, Saint Catherine of Siena and a Carthusian Monk*, probably painted during the years of his intense activity at the Pavia Charterhouse (1488-94), and *Madonna del Velo*, a refined and extremely delicate work dating from the latter part of the artist's career.

Gian Pietro Rizzi, called Giampietrino
(Milan, documented in the first half of the 16th century)
The Magdalen seated in Prayer
Oil on panel, 50x60
Donated in 1835 by Giulia Beccaria, mother of Alessandro Manzoni.

Bartolomeo Veneto
(active between 1502 and the 1530)
Lute Player
Oil on panel, 65x50
Acquired in 1932.

Giovanni Antonio Boltraffio
(Milan 1467 – 1516)
Portrait of Gerolamo Casio
Oil on panel, 52x43
In Brera since 1902, originally in the Library of Bologna University.

Lombard painter
(beginning of the 16th century)
Two Devotees in Adoration
Oil on panel, 140x120
Fragment. Acquired in 1897.

Andrea Solario
(Milan ca. 1470 – 1524)
Portrait of a Young Man
Tempera and oil on panel, 42x32
In Brera since 1811, originally in the Archbishop's Palace at Milan (bequest of Cardinal Cesare Monti).

Giovanni Ambrose De Predis
(Milan ca. 1455 – after 1508)
Portrait of a Young Man
Oil on panel, 49x39

Giovanni Agostino da Lodi
(Lombardy, active from the last decade of the 15th century to ca. 1520)
Saints Peter and John the Evangelist
Oil on panel, 26x35
Signed. Acquired in 1913.

Ambrose da Fossano, called Bergognone
(Milan ca. 1453 – 1523)
Madonna and Child, Saint Catherine of Siena and a Carthusian Monk
Oil on panel, 46x40·5
Acquired in 1891 from the collection of Carlo Henfrey of Baveno.
It is thought that Bergognone painted it for the cell of a monk at the Charterhouse of Pavia, where he worked from 1488 to 1494.

Bergognone
Madonna with Sleeping Child (Madonna del Velo)
Oil on panel, 60x40
Acquired in 1911 from a private individual.
This *Madonna* too seems to have been painted for a cell in the Charterhouse of Pavia, judging by the two seated monks in the little scene in the background, but in a later period of the artist's career.

Andrea Solario
Madonna and Child with Saints Joseph and Simeon
Tempera and oil on panel transferred onto canvas, 102x87
Signed and dated 1495.
Donated in 1811 by Eugène de Beauharnais.

Bernardino Luini (?)
(Milan 1480/90 – 1532)
Madonna and Child, Saints James and Philip and the Busti Family
Oil on panel, 195x145
In Brera since 1809, originally in the church of Santa Maria di Brera.

Bernardino Luini
Madonna del Roseto
Oil on panel, 70x63
In Brera since 1825, originally in the Pavia Charterhouse.

Cesare da Sesto
(Sesto Calende, Varese, 1477 – Milan 1523)
Madonna dell'Albero
Oil on panel, 46x36
Entered Brera before 1812.

Follower of Leonardo
(Lombardy, 16th century)
Madonna and Child with Lamb
Oil on panel, 60x52
Acquired in 1893.

Bergognone, *Madonna and Child, Saint Catherine of Siena and a Carthusian Monk.*

Facing page: Bergognone, *Madonna with Sleeping Child (Madonna del Velo).*

Bernardino Luini, *Madonna del Roseto.*

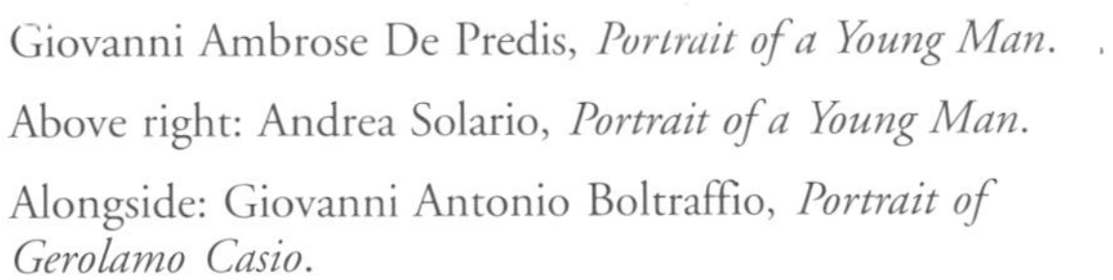

Giovanni Ambrose De Predis, *Portrait of a Young Man.*

Above right: Andrea Solario, *Portrait of a Young Man.*

Alongside: Giovanni Antonio Boltraffio, *Portrait of Gerolamo Casio.*

Room XX

Emilian art is fairly well represented in the Pinacoteca di Brera, and this room offers a selection of the most important painters who were active in that region in the late fifteenth century and the first few decades of the sixteenth.
A small *Christ Crucified*, fragment of an altarpiece with *Saint Jerome* now in the National Gallery in London, is by Cosmè Tura, an outstanding exponent of the Ferrarese school.
There are also two splendid pictures of *Saint Peter* and *Saint John the Baptist* by Francesco del Cossa, an artist who was fascinated by the style of Piero della Francesca and open to the influence of Mantegna. These two paintings are truly emblematic of the manner of this great Ferrarese painter, who was fond of the meticulous and almost obsessive description of even the tiniest of objects, bathed in a limpid and transparent light, and yet did not lose sight of the vibrant qualities of the skin and the full and monumental forms of the drapery.
Lorenzo Costa – along with that other great painter Francesco Francia – was one of the most significant representatives of what is usually described as the "early Emilian classicism" of the first few decades of the sixteenth century. Here we see his *Adoration of the Magi*, characteristic of a fairly advanced phase of his production. After 1500, in fact, following a training grounded in Ferrarese artistic circles, he absorbed certain ideas derived from Perugino and Filippino Lippi, moving toward an eclectic style of painting in which great importance was given to the layout of the composition.
A contemporary of Costa and Francia was the Bolognese Amico Aspertini. He was an unusual artist, interested in the accentuation of features, whose entire output was imbued with an air of the fabulous, as can be seen in this picture of *Saint Cassian*.

Ferrarese master
(active around 1450)
The Merchants who had Stolen the Ass begging Forgiveness from Saint Jerome
The Ailing Saint Jerome sees Himself flogged before Christ
Panels, 41x30 (each)

Filippo Mazzola
(Parma ca. 1460 – 1505)
Portrait of a Man
Oil on panel, 44x28
Signed. In Brera since 1811, originally in the Archbishop's Palace at Milan (bequest of Cardinal Cesare Monti).

Lorenzo Leonbruno
(Mantua ca. 1477 – 1537)
Allegory of Calumny
Oil on panel, 76x100
Signed. Monochrome.

Venetian painter
(active around 1480)
Portrait of a Man
Portrait of a Woman
Tempera on panel, 25x18 (each)
Originally painted on the front and back of a single panel, then sawed in two. In Brera since 1894 by exchange with the Bologna University.

Emilian painter (Gian Francesco Maineri?)
(end of the 15th century)
Flagellation
Canvas, 66x50

Bernardino Zaganelli
(Cotignola, Ravenna, 1460/70 – after 1509)
Christ carrying the Cross
Oil on panel, 37x31

Bernardino Zaganelli
Christ carrying the Cross
Oil on panel, 95x55
On deposit from the Litta Modignani collection.

Marco Palmezzano
(Forlì 1459/63 – 1539)
Head of Saint John the Baptist
Oil on panel, 29x26
In Brera since 1811, originally in the Observant church at Cotignola (Ravenna).

Gian Francesco Maineri
(Parma, documented from 1489 to 1506)
Head of Saint John the Baptist
Oil on panel transferred onto canvas, 44x30
Signed.

Lorenzo Costa
(Ferrara ca. 1460 – Mantua 1535)
Adoration of the Magi
Oil on panel, 75x181
Signed and dated 1499.
Predella of the *Nativity* by Francesco Francia, now in the Pinacoteca di Bologna.

Amico Aspertini
(Bologna ca. 1474/75 – 1552)
Saint Cassian
Panel, 34x38

Francesco del Cossa
(Ferrara ca. 1436 – Bologna ca. 1478)
Saint John the Baptist
Saint Peter
Tempera and gold on panel, 112x55 (each)
The two panels come from a polyptych devoted to the Spanish Dominican St. Vincent Ferrer, once located in the chapel of the Griffoni family, in San Petronio at Bologna. The work was broken up between 1725 and 1730 when the chapel was renovated by Stefano Orlandi. The drawings made by the latter before starting work have proved an invaluable source of information on the original composition and location of the polyptych. The central panel depicting *Saint Vincent Ferrer* is in the National Gallery in London.

Cosmè Tura
(Ferrara ca. 1430 – 1495)
Christ Crucified
Tempera on panel, 22x17
Fragment of an altarpiece with *Saint Jerome*, once in the Ferrara Charterhouse, now in part in the National Gallery at London.

Amico Aspertini, *Saint Cassian*.

Above: Lorenzo Costa, *Adoration of the Magi*.

Francesco del Cossa,
Saint Peter.

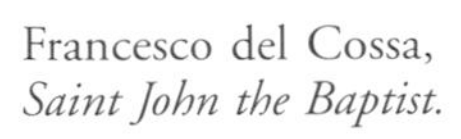

Francesco del Cossa,
Saint John the Baptist.

Room XXI

Venetian by birth but an inhabitant of the Marche by choice, Carlo Crivelli painted some of his finest works in this region. Characterized by a fanciful and intellectual style, they are amply represented at Brera. The *Camerino Triptych*, signed and dated 1482, is a typical example of his mature language, in which it is possible to discern a degree of adaptation to Renaissance formulas, as in the attempt at a spatial unification of the various panels and the presence of decorative elements drawn from the classical repertory. The *Madonna della Candeletta* dates from slightly later (1490-91) and also comes from Camerino, where it formed the central part of a polyptych painted for the cathedral, like the other panel with the *Crucifixion* (also in this room), which may have formed the cymatium. Both reflect a phase in Crivelli's output that was marked by a stagnation in his stock of forms, which were continually reused. Yet it is difficult to resist the fascination of such lavish decoration, in which the customary festoons of plants encircle the luxurious damasks of the fabrics and the precious marble of the throne.

His last known work, painted shortly before his death, is the *Coronation of the Virgin*, once surmounted by the lunette with the *Pietà*.

Other painters active in the Marche were Girolamo di Giovanni, whose *Gualdo Tadino Polyptych*, displayed in this room, is one of the artist's finest works, and Pietro Alemanno, a little-known artist – he may have come to the Marche with Crivelli – who painted the polyptych we see here for the church of San Francesco at Monterubbiano.

Vittore Crivelli
(Venice ca. 1440 – Fermo 1501)
Saints Jinesius and Joachim
Saints Ann and Francis
Tempera on panel, 134x60 and 134x65
In Brera since 1855, bequest from Pietro Oggioni.

Vittore Crivelli
Saint John the Evangelist
Tempera on panel, 132x50
Compartment of a polyptych now broken up. In Brera since 1855, bequest from Pietro Oggioni.

Carlo Crivelli
(Venice 1430/35 – Fermo, ca. 1495)
Camerino Triptych
Tempera on panel
Central panel, 190x78: *Madonna and Child* (signed and dated 1482)
Side panels, 170x60 (each): *Saints Peter and Dominic* and *Saints Peter Martyr and Venantius*
Lower panels, 25x62 (each): *Saints James, Bernardine and Peregrine* and *Saints Anthony Abbot, Jerome and Andrew*
Originally in the church of San Domenico at Camerino.

Carlo Crivelli
Coronation of the Virgin
Tempera on panel, 255x225
In the lunette: *The Dead Christ*
Signed and dated 1493.
Originally in the church of San Francesco at Fabriano.

Carlo Crivelli
Madonna della Candeletta
Oil on panel, 218x75
Signed.
It was part of a polyptych painted for Camerino Cathedral, from which it was removed following the earthquake in 1799 and transferred to the church of San Domenico. It was removed from there and sent to Brera in 1811. In addition to the *Crucifixion*, the original polyptych – painted after 1488 – was made up of two panels that are now in the Gallerie dell'Accademia in Venice.

Carlo Crivelli
Christ Crucified with the Virgin and Saint John the Evangelist
Oil on panel, 218x75
Part of the dismembered polyptych originally in Camerino Cathedral (Santa Maria Maggiore).

Pietro Alemanno
(Göttweih, active in the Marche from 1475 to 1497)
Monterubbiano Polyptych
Tempera on panel
Lower central panel, 108x51: *Madonna and Child*
Upper central panel, 62x49: *Resurrection*
Lower side panels, 146x33 (each): *Saints Augustine, Peter, John the Baptist and Francis*
Upper side panels, 58x29 (each): *Saints Jerome, Pope Cornelius, Louis of Toulouse and Stephen*
In Brera since 1811, originally in the church of San Francesco at Monterubbiano (Ascoli Piceno).

Niccolò di Liberatore, called Alunno
(Foligno, ca. 1430 – 1502)
Cagli Polyptych
Tempera on panel
Lower central panel, 178x91: *Madonna Enthroned and Child with Angels*
Upper central panel, 121x91: *Christ Risen and Angels*
Lower side panels, 157x47 (each): *Saints Sebastian, Francis, Bernardine of Siena and Louis of Toulouse*
Upper side panels: *Saint Peter* (107x47); *Saint John the Baptist* (91x47); *Saint Anthony of Padua* (99x47); *Saint Jerome* (95x47)
Cusps, 60x41 (each): *Saints Clare and Peter Martyr*
Originally in the monastery of San Francesco at Cagli (Pesaro).

Bartolomeo di Tommaso
(Marche, active from 1425 to 1455)
Virgin adoring the Child
Tempera on panel, 121x42
In Brera since 1811, originally in the church of San Giacomo at Pergola (Pesaro).

Girolamo di Giovanni
(Camerino, documented from 1449 to 1473)
Gualdo Tadino Polyptych
Tempera on panel
Lower central panel, 132x60: *Madonna and Child with Angels*
Upper central panel, 190x60: *Crucifixion*
Lower side panels, 118x42 (each): *Saints Augustine, Catherine, Apollonia and Nicholas of Tolentino*
Upper side panels, 154x42 (each): *Saints Sebastian, Peter, Lawrence and Jerome*
On deposit from the Museo Poldi Pezzoli in Milan. Originally in the church of Sant'Agostino at Gualdo Tadino (Perugia), reassembled in 1925.

Master of the Barberini Panels
(documented from 1445 to 1484)
Saint Peter
Tempera on panel, 140x48
In Brera since 1904/05, bequest from Casimiro Sipriot.

Carlo Crivelli, *Coronation of the Virgin*.

Above: Carlo Crivelli, *The Dead Christ*.

Pietro Alemanno, *Monterubbiano Polyptych.*

Below: Carlo Crivelli, *Camerino Triptych.*

Carlo Crivelli, *Christ Crucified with the Virgin and Saint John the Evangelist.*

Carlo Crivelli, *Madonna della Candeletta.*

Rooms XXII and XXIII

The paintings on show in these two rooms are by artists active in Emilia Romagna between the end of the fifteenth century and the beginning of the sixteenth, such as Francesco and Bernardino Zaganelli, Garofalo and Marco Palmezzano. It is worth singling out a *Madonna and Child with Saints* by the latter, a signed and dated (1493) work that marks an important stage in the evolution of his style, distinguished by a well-defined spatiality and a solidity in the figures, perhaps derived from his contacts with contemporary sculptors.
Brera possesses one of the most significant works by the Ferrarese painter Ercole de' Roberti, the imposing altarpiece representing a *Madonna and Child with Saints* that was originally in the church of Santa Maria in Porto at Ravenna. The composition has a fully Renaissance breadth and the *Sacra Conversazione* is set inside a complex architectural structure of great harmony, but richly decorated in the typical Ferrarese manner, with mock bronze bas-reliefs representing historical scenes. The picture is very important, partly because it is the only one in de' Roberti's catalogue for which there is documentary evidence of the date at which it was painted, around 1480: thus the work shows the evolution of the artist's style after the celebrated frescoes in Palazzo di Schifanoia at Ferrara and the *San Lazzaro Altarpiece*, formerly in the Kaiser Friedrich Museum at Berlin and unfortunately destroyed in 1945.
Another Ferrarese painter, but belonging to the following generation, is Dosso Dossi. Here we see his elegant picture of *Saint Sebastian*, emblematic of his mature work when the Giorgionesque influences of his youth – of which traces can still be discerned in the fine landscape on the left – were overlaid by more recent cultural experiences that emphasized drawing and the plastic definition of bodies.
The selection of works by Emilian artists continues in room XXIII, with paintings like the *Annunciation* by Francesco Raibolini, called Francia, one of the principal exponents of the Bolognese classicist current of the early sixteenth century. There are two works by Correggio, who was active chiefly at Parma: a *Nativity* painted while the artist was in Mantua and which resembles the *San Francesco Madonna* now in the Gemäldegalerie at Dresden, owing to the presence of elements derived from Mantegna but considerably softened, and a richly colored *Adoration of the Magi*, datable to around 1516.

Room XXII

Giovanni Luteri, called Dosso Dossi
(Ferrara? ca. 1489 – Ferrara 1542)
Saint John the Baptist
Saint George
Oil on panel, 163x49 e 163x48
Parts of a triptych. Acquired in 1903.

Giovanni Battista Benvenuti, called Ortolano
(Ferrara ca. 1487 – 1525)
Crucifixion
Oil on panel, 258x176
In Brera since 1905, originally in the church of Sant'Agostino at Ferrara.

Benvenuto Tisi, called Garofalo
(Ferrara ca. 1476 – 1559)
Christ Deposed
Oil on panel, 300x166
In Brera since 1811, originally in the church of Sant'Antonio in Polesine at Ferrara.

Dosso Dossi
Saint Sebastian
Oil on panel, 182x95
In Brera since 1808, originally in the church of the Santissima Annunziata at Cremona.

Lodovico Mazzolino
(Ferrara 1480 – 1528)
Raising of Lazarus
Oil on panel, 38x50
Dated 1527.

Ercole de' Roberti
(Ferrara ca. 1450 – 1496)
Madonna Enthroned and Child with Saints Ann, Elizabeth and Augustine and the Blessed Pietro degli Onesti
Oil on canvas, 323x240
In Brera since 1811. Originally in the main chapel of the church of Santa Maria in Porto Fuori at Ravenna, it was later (ca. 1550) transferred, along with the Lateran canons to which the work refers, to the church of Santa Maria in Porto, inside the city walls. At the foot of the throne, on the right, is portrayed the Blessed Piero degli Onesti, who founded Santa Maria in Porto Fuori in fulfillment of a vow made to the Virgin when he had been saved from a shipwreck on his return from a pilgrimage to the Holy Land. The landscape that is visible between the columns of the throne may be a representation of the port of Ravenna during a storm.

Geminiano Benzoni
(Emilia, documented from 1489 to 1513)
Saint Paul
Oil on panel, 52x37
Donated by Anna Fumagalli Sessa in 1932.

Niccolò Pisano
(Pisa 1470 – 1538)
Madonna and Child
Oil on panel, 40x34
In Brera since 1904.

Marco Palmezzano
(Forlì 1459/63 – 1539)
Adoration of the Child
Oil on panel, 227x135
Signed and dated 1492 (?).
In Brera since 1809, originally in the confraternity of the Bianchi di Valverde at Forlì.

Girolamo Marchesi
(Cotignola, Ravenna, 1480? – Bologna after 1531)
The Deposition of Christ
Oil on panel transferred onto canvas, 172x148

Marco Palmezzano
Coronation of the Virgin with Saints Francis and Benedict
Oil on panel, 160x125
Signed. In Brera since 1811, originally in the Observant church at Cotignola (Ravenna).

Marco Palmezzano
Madonna and Child with Saints John the Baptist, Peter, Dominic and Mary Magdalene
Oil on panel, 170x158
Signed and dated 1493. In Brera since 1809, originally in the confraternity of the Bianchi di Valverde at Forlì.

Dosso Dossi, *Saint Sebastian.*

Niccolò Rondinelli
(Ravenna ca. 1450 – ca. 1510)
Madonna and Child with Saints Nicholas, Peter, Bartholomew and Augustine
Oil on panel, 269x220
In Brera since 1811, originally in San Domenico at Ravenna.

Francesco Zaganelli
(Cotignola, Ravenna, ca. 1460/70 – Ravenna 1532)
and **Bernardino Zaganelli**
(Cotignola, Ravenna, ca. 1460/70 – after 1509)
Madonna and Child with Saints John the Baptist and Florian
Oil on panel, 197x160
In Brera since 1899.

Room XXIII

Antonio Allegri, called Correggio
(Correggio, Reggio Emilia, 1489 – 1534)
The Nativity
Oil on panel, 79x100
In Brera since 1913, originally in the Benigno Crespi collection.

Marco Palmezzano, *Madonna and Child with Saints.*

Michelangelo Anselmi
(Lucca ca. 1492 – Parma ca. 1554)
Saints Jerome and Catherine of Alexandria
Oil on canvas, 155x110
In Brera since 1901, originally in the church of San Francesco del Prato at Parma.

Correggio
Adoration of the Magi
Oil on canvas, 84x108
In Brera since 1895, originally in the Archbishop's Palace at Milan (bequest of Cardinal Monti).

Francesco Raibolini, called Francia
(Bologna ca. 1450 – 1517)
The Annunciation
Tempera on panel transferred onto canvas, 237x227
Originally in the church of San Francesco at Mantua.

Ercole de' Roberti, *Madonna Enthroned and Child with Saints and the Blessed Pietro degli Onesti.*

Correggio, *Adoration of the Magi*.

Correggio, *The Nativity*.

Piero della Francesca and Raphael Room

Here we can find some of the masterpieces that are the pride of the Pinacoteca di Brera.
First of all, the *Madonna and Saints with the Donor Federico da Montefeltro*, also known as the *Brera Madonna* and originally painted for the high altar of the church of San Bernardino in Urbino. It is a work of capital importance in the painter's artistic development, imbued with the knowledge of perspective that he had assimilated in his youth at Florence, when he worked with Domenico Veneziano on the lost frescoes in the church of Sant'Egidio.
Here the achievements of his early years – a perfect balance of form, light and color – are fused with the influence of Flemish painting, which is apparent in the meticulous representation of the figures and architecture. The curious motif of the egg hanging from the shell is a reference, in the language of medieval mysticism, to the conception of Christ through the Holy Spirit.
Raphael's *Betrothal of the Virgin*, often known by its Italian name of *Lo Sposalizio*, marks the end of the artist's juvenile period. Signed and dated 1504, it is a composition based on celebrated works by his master, Perugino, such as the fresco depicting the *Handing over of the Keys* in the Sistine Chapel. Raphael gives the setting a broader sweep than in Perugino's models, however, making the small temple the pivot of the composition. In this way the handling of perspective allows the figures – defined by precise drawing and a transparent light – a great freedom of movement in space.
The *Christ at the Column* (from the abbey of Chiaravalle) is one of the few surviving paintings by Donato Bramante. The picture clearly shows the fundamentals of perspective that the artist developed through his contacts with the court of Urbino, but also the influence of Leonardo in the precise definition of the human body and perhaps in the fine landscape in the background. Characteristic of Bramante are the attempt to represent the figure in an illusionistic manner – as if it were a sculpture – and the presence of decorative motifs in a classical style, which can also be seen in such architectural works as the church of Santa Maria presso San Satiro at Milan.
The painter Luca Signorelli from Cortona is represented here by a *Madonna and Child* and a *Flagellation of Christ*, which originally formed two sides of a processional standard. The iconography of the *Flagellation*, which was on the back of the standard, was inspired by Piero della Francesca's picture of the same subject, in Urbino. In contrast with Piero's painting, however, Signorelli emphasizes plastic and spatial values over those of perspective, as can be seen in the twisted naked bodies of the torturers, illuminated by an almost tangential light that brings out their musculature.

Piero della Francesca
(Borgo San Sepolcro ca. 1415 – 1492)
Madonna and Saints with the Donor Federico da Montefeltro
Panel, 251x172
In Brera since 1811, it was formerly on the high altar of the church of San Bernardino near Urbino.
The original location of this painting is disputed, though it may have been in the church of San Donato dell'Osservanza (Federico da Montefeltro's burial place) and then moved to the church of San Bernardino. The date is equally controversial: historians have assigned it to anywhere between the end of the 1470s and the late 1480s. The picture, often referred to as the best example of Sacra Conversazione in the XV century, represents the meeting of the donor, Duke Federico da Montefeltro of Urbino, with the Virgin Mary, who is ringed by six saints: John the Baptist, Bernardine and Jerome on the left, Francesco, Peter the Martyr and another saint (John the Evangelist?) holding a richly bound book on the right. Four archangels with precious necklaces stand alongside the Madonna, whose bonnet also used to be adorned with a large jewel, as has been revealed by X-ray photographs.
The donor kneeling on the right of Mary is wearing a gleaming and detailed suit of armor (you can even see the reflection of a window in it). This has been identified as of Milanese manufacture, from the school of the Missaglia.

Raffaello Sanzio, called Raphael
(Urbino 1483 – Rome 1520)
Betrothal of the Virgin (Lo Sposalizio)
Oil on panel, 170x118
Signed and dated 1504.
In Brera since 1806.
Commissioned by the Albizzini family for the chapel of San Giuseppe in the church of San Francesco at Città di Castello, it remained there until 1798 when the government of the city was obliged to donate it to Giuseppe Lechi, a general in the Napoleonic army, as a token of gratitude. Three years later it was sold to the Milanese collector Conte Sannazzari who in 1804 bequeathed it to the Ospedale Maggiore in Milan. In 1805 it was purchased for the Pinacoteca.
The pivot of the painting, one of the artist's early masterpieces, is the polygonal temple, which is reminiscent of Bramante's architecture. It serves to link the splendid marble square drawn in accordance with Piero della Francesca's *De prospectiva pingendi* and the group of figures arranged in perfect symmetry along tangent semicircles.

Donato Bramante
(Fermignano, Pesaro, 1444 – Rome 1514)
Christ at the Column
Panel, 93·7x 62·5
In Brera since 1915, on deposit from the abbey of Chiaravalle at Milan.

Piero della Francesca, *Madonna and Saints with the Donor Federico da Montefeltro.*

Luca Signorelli
(Cortona ca. 1450 – 1523)
The Flagellation of Jesus
Madonna del Latte
Tempera on panel, 84x60 (each)
It is likely that the two panels, front and back of a processional standard, originally came from the old Confraternita dei Raccomandati, which had a chapel in the church of Santa Maria del Mercato at Fabriano. The members of this confraternity dedicated themselves to works of charity and welfare and carried out acts of devotion by taking part in processions dressed in sackcloth and carrying devotional standards and plaques.
The theme of the *Madonna del Latte* (*Madonna of the Milk*) was linked with the role played by the Oblates of Santa Maria del Mercato, who took care of abandoned children. The Madonna uncovering her breast and offering it to the Child, who in turn points it out to the devotee, is a symbol of Christian charity and the wet nurse.

Luca Signorelli, *The Flagellation of Jesus.*

Below: Luca Signorelli, *Madonna del Latte.*

Facing page: Raphael, *Betrothal of the Virgin (Lo Sposalizio).*

RAPHAEL·VRBINAS
M DIIII

Donato Bramante, *Christ at the Column*.

Room XXVII

There are not many works by Mannerist painters in Brera. The *Portrait of Andrea Doria as Neptune* is undoubtedly one of the finest works of the Florentine Agnolo Bronzino, whose style is characterized by a tendency toward lucid and objective representation, by a purity of form, and by the use of a cold and limpid light. The work is an original one from the iconographic viewpoint as well, and shows the marked influence of Michelangelo's statuary, in particular the *Moses* in San Pietro in Vincoli.
Salviati was another Florentine by birth, but moved as a young man to Rome, where he became one of the leading lights of the city's artistic scene, as well as a bridge between the Florentine Mannerism of his training and the Roman manner, dominated by the personality of Raphael.
Raphael's influence can also be detected in the large panel by Girolamo Genga (*Madonna and Child, Saints and the Doctors of the Church*), a complex work that combines many different sources of inspiration and that is characterized as a whole by a sort of personal Mannerist style.

Giovanni Antonio Sogliani
(Florence 1492 – 1544)
Saint Catherine of Alexandria
Oil on panel, 82x67
Signed. Donated in 1978 by the friends of Franco Russoli.

Pietro di Giovanni Bonaccorsi, called Perin del Vaga
(Florence 1501 – Rome 1547)
The Crossing of the Red Sea
Canvas, monochrome, 118x201
Acquired in 1826.

Agnolo Bronzino
(Monticelli, Florence, 1503 – Florence 1572)
Andrea Doria as Neptune
Oil on canvas, 115x53
This painting used to be in the collection of portraits of illustrious men that belonged to the writer Paolo Giovio from Como. Vasari states that it was painted by Bronzino at the time of his return to Florence from Pesaro. It can therefore be dated to the years 1531-33. The representation of the Genoese admiral in the guise of Neptune had a precedent in a bronze statue that the republic of Genoa (1528) had commissioned from Baccio Bandinelli, and seems also to have been influenced by the similar portrait painted by Sebastiano del Piombo, now in the Galleria Doria Pamphilj at Rome.

Agnolo Bronzino,
Andrea Doria as Neptune.

Girolamo Genga, *Madonna and Child, Saints and the Doctors of the Church.*

Facing page: Francesco Salviati, *Lamentation.*

Francesco de' Rossi, called Salviati
(Florence 1510 – Rome 1563)
Lamentation
Oil on canvas, 322x193
In Brera since 1811, originally in the church of the Corpus Domini at Venice.

Luca Signorelli
(Cortona ca. 1450 – 1523)
Madonna and Child Enthroned with Saints James, Simon, Francis and Bonaventure
Tempera on panel, 227x185
Signed and dated 1508.
In Brera since 1811, originally in the Filippini Chapel of the church of San Francesco at Arcevia (Ancona).

Timoteo Viti
(Urbino 1469 – 1523)
The Virgin and Saints Sebastian and John the Baptist
Oil on panel, 260x182

Girolamo Genga
(Urbino ca. 1476 – 1551)
Madonna and Child, Saints and the Doctors of the Church
Oil on panel, 438x290
In Brera since 1809, originally in the church of Sant'Agostino at Cesena (Forlì).

Room XXVIII

This room houses a group of paintings by seventeenth-century artists belonging to the Bolognese school. The true founders of this school were Annibale, Ludovico and Agostino Carracci, who set up the Accademia dei Desiderosi (later Accademia degli Incamminati) at the end of the sixteenth century. This teaching academy set out to renew painting by abandoning the formulas of Mannerism and returning to nature, though without forgetting the great lesson of the masters of the Cinquecento.
The eldest of the three was Ludovico, who was also director of the academy and therefore had the opportunity to teach many painters of the following generation. Here we can see his *Christ and the Woman of Canaan*, a picture painted at a time when he showed a great affinity for the classicist style of Annibale, and the *Adoration of the Magi*, a canvas from his later maturity when the artist seemed to turn back to the more intimate and popular characteristics of his early work. Of the three, Annibale Carracci was the one who spent most time outside Bologna, but it was he who made the greatest contribution to the renewal of Bolognese pictorial language. This is clear from the canvas depicting the *Samaritan Woman at the Well*, whose stylistic similarities with other works, such as the *Resurrection* (1593) in the Louvre, suggest that it was probably painted around 1593-94.
The Carracci had important pupils in both Bologna and Rome. One of them was the Bolognese Guido Reni, who painted the splendid picture of *Saints Peter and Paul*, in which ideals of harmonious composition and formal rigor are blended with a study of nature derived from the Carracci.
The youngest of the Carracci's pupils was Giovan Francesco Barbieri, called Guercino, an artist who immediately showed a marked inclination toward naturalistic representation. His style, based on large areas of color produced by laying on very liquid paint with rapid and vibrant brushstrokes, is clearly apparent in the fine canvas depicting *Abraham repudiating Hagar*, which can be dated to the latter part of his career.

Guido Reni
(Bologna 1575 – 1642)
Saints Peter and Paul
Oil on canvas, 197x140
In Brera since 1811, originally in the Sampieri collection at Bologna.

Giovan Francesco Barbieri, called Guercino
(Cento, Ferrara, 1591 – Bologna 1666)
Abraham repudiating Hagar
Oil on canvas, 115x152
In Brera since 1811, originally in the Sampieri collection at Bologna. The picture was commissioned (1657) by the community of Cento as a gift to Cardinal Lorenzo Imperiali, legate of Ferrara.

Ludovico Carracci
(Bologna 1555 – 1619)
Saint Anthony Abbot preaching to the Hermits
Oil on canvas, 320x210
In Brera since 1809, originally in the church of Sant'Antonio Abate at Bologna.

Francesco Gessi
(Bologna 1588 – 1649)
Madonna and Child with Saints Lawrence, Nicholas and Frances of Rome
Oil on canvas, 238x153·5
In Brera since 1809, originally in the church of Santa Maria dei Poveri at Crevalcore (Modena).

Annibale Carracci
(Bologna 1560 – Rome 1609)
The Samaritan Woman at the Well
Oil on canvas, 170x225
In Brera since 1811, originally in the Sampieri collection at Bologna.

Ludovico Carracci
Christ and the Woman of Canaan
Oil on canvas, 170x225
In Brera since 1811, originally in the Sampieri collection at Bologna.

Ludovico Carracci
Adoration of the Magi
Oil on canvas, 260x175
Signed and dated 1616. In Brera since 1809, originally in the church of Santa Maria dei Battisti at Crevalcore (Modena).

Federico Fiori, called Barocci
(Urbino 1528 – 1612)
Martyrdom of Saint Vitalis
Oil on canvas, 302x268
Signed and dated 1583. In Brera since 1811, originally in the church of San Vitale at Ravenna.

Guido Reni, *Saints Peter and Paul.*

Guercino, *Abraham repudiating Hagar.*

Annibale Carracci, *The Samaritan Woman at the Well.*

Room XXIX

This small room contains Caravaggio's celebrated picture of the *Supper at Emmaus* (ca. 1606). In comparison with the painting of the same subject now in the National Gallery in London – dating from almost a decade earlier – Caravaggio uses a darker setting for the scene, emphasizing the emotional component by skillful use of light and shadow rather than by obvious gestures.
In addition to this important picture, the room houses a series of works by followers of Caravaggio. Among them, a highly significant role was played by the Neapolitan Battistello Caracciolo – whose *Samaritan Woman at the Well* is on show here. He was one of the first painters to adopt Merisi's innovations and above all to grasp the importance given to luministic values in his work. Caravaggio's naturalism and luminism were taken to almost exaggerated extremes by Jusepe de Ribera called Spagnoletto, a Spanish artist who worked in Naples. His style is characterized by a crude realism and an emphasis on violent and often macabre details, as in the *Penitent Saint Jerome*, which some critics believe to be his own work while others attribute it to his studio.
Orazio Gentileschi, an artist of Pisan origin but who was active in Roman circles, painted the canvas depicting *The Martyrs Valerian, Tiburtius and Cecily*, considered one of his works most closely modeled on Caravaggio, and in particular on the *Death of the Virgin* in the Louvre.
The more Caravaggesque phase of the painter Mattia Preti, who displays a style that is already baroque, is well-exemplified by the picture of *A Mother entrusting her Children to the Redeemer*. This artist generally used effects of grazing light derived from Caravaggio, adapting them to crowded compositions or scenes with figures in constant movement, often with architectural backdrops.

Mattia Preti
(Taverna, Catanzaro, 1613 – Valletta 1699)
A Mother entrusting her Children to the Redeemer
Oil on canvas, 143x193
Donated in 1812 by Eugène de Beauharnais.

School of Caravaggio
Saint Sebastian
Oil on canvas, 134x99
In Brera since 1811, originally in the Archbishop's Palace at Milan (bequest of Cardinal Cesare Monti).

Orazio Gentileschi
(Pisa 1563 – London 1639)
The Martyrs Valerian, Tiburtius and Cecily
Oil on canvas, 350x218
Formerly in the church di Santa Cecilia at Como.

Giovan Battista Caracciolo, called Battistello
(Naples 1578 – 1635)
The Samaritan Woman at the Well
Oil on canvas, 200x165
Initialed: GB.A. In Brera since 1820 by exchange.

Jusepe de Ribera, called Spagnoletto
(Játiva 1591 – Naples 1652)
Penitent Saint Jerome
Oil on canvas, 109x82
Acquired in 1886.

Mattia Preti
Saint Peter paying the Tribute Money
Oil on canvas, 143x193
Donated in 1812 by Eugène de Beauharnais.

Michelangelo Merisi, called Caravaggio
(Caravaggio, Bergamo, 1573 – Porto Ercole 1610)
Supper at Emmaus
Oil on canvas, 141x175
Donated in 1939 by the Friends of Brera.
The canvas was acquired by Marchese Patrizi as early as 1624. It represents the most mature period in Caravaggio's artistic career, and can therefore be dated to 1605-6.

Orazio Gentileschi, *The Martyrs Valerian, Tiburtius and Cecily.*

Caravaggio, *Supper at Emmaus.*

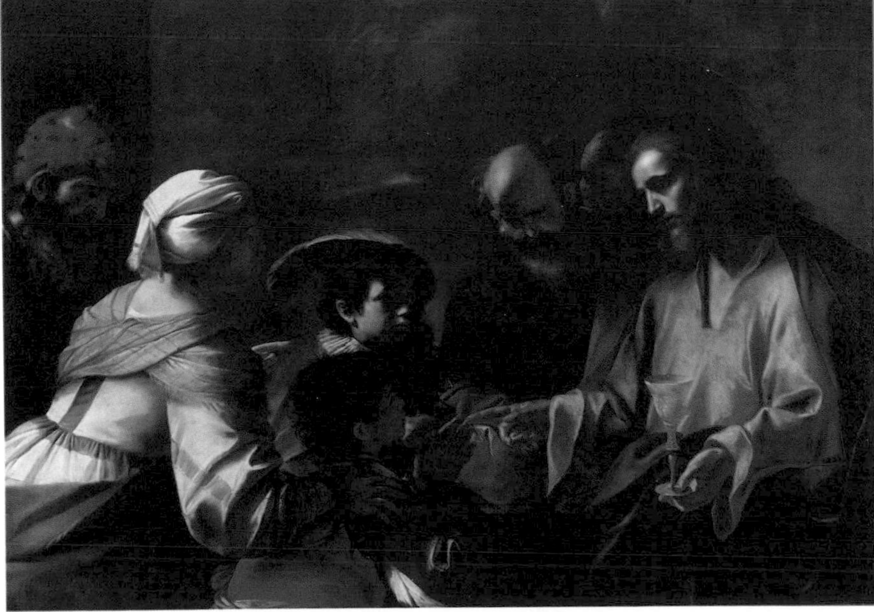

Mattia Preti, *A Mother entrusting her Children to the Redeemer.*

Room XXX

This small room presents a selection of pictures painted by Lombard artists operating in the seventeenth century. They include Giulio Cesare Procaccini, originally from Bologna but active in Milan. Several of his canvases are on show here, outstanding among them the *Mystic Marriage of Saint Catherine*. This painting – like the *Magdalen* – belongs to a large group of works for private devotion that he started to paint in the middle of the second decade of the century, in which it is possible to discern the influence of Emilian Mannerism and a tendency to a multifaceted handling of the paint, especially where the drapery is concerned.
A contemporary of Procaccini was Giovan Battista Crespi, called Cerano, an artist who still displays a degree of Mannerism in his use of highly studied attitudes and poses. His intense *Madonna del Rosario* is the work that best reflects the climate of the Lombard Counter Reformation in which Cerano played a dominant role.
Piero Francesco Mazzucchelli, known as Morazzone, belonged to the same generation. He is famous for the beautiful frescoes in the chapels of the Sacri Monti at Varese, Orta and Varallo, paintings of great naturalism and brutal realism in a style similar to that of the canvas representing *Saint Francis in Ecstasy*.
The room contains an interesting collaboration by the three aforementioned artists, the canvas depicting the *Martyrdom of Saints Rufina and Seconda*, which is known for this reason as the "three-hand painting."
The following generation is represented by Francesco Cairo, an artist whose style is characterized by a marked sentimentalism and the enervated languor of his figures (*Christ in the Garden*), and Daniele Crespi, a pupil of Cerano, whose *Last Supper*, based on the one painted by Gaudenzio Ferrari for Santa Maria della Passione, is on show here. Toward the end of his career, in fact, the artist tended to paint new versions of well-known pictures, making use of a naturalistic classicism of forms and a very marked expressiveness, in which the preeminent role was given to drawing.

Antonio d'Enrico, called Tanzio da Varallo
(Riale d'Alagna, Vercelli, ca. 1580 – Varallo Sesia, Vercelli, 1632/33)
The Martyrdom of the Franciscans at Nagasaki
Oil on canvas, 115x80
In Brera since 1811, originally in the monastery of the Grazie at Varallo.

Francesco Cairo
(Milan 1607 – 1665)
Christ in the Garden
Oil on canvas, 76x62
Donated in 1964 by the Friends of Brera, originally in the Cugini collection at Bergamo.

Pier Francesco Mazzucchelli, called Morazzone
(Morazzone, Varese, 1573 – before May 1626)
Saint Francis
Oil on canvas, 99x75
Donated in 1949 by Paolo D'Ancona.

Daniele Crespi
(Busto Arsizio 1597/1600 – Milan 1630)
Last Supper
Oil on canvas, 335x220
In Brera since 1805, originally in the Benedictine monastery at Brugora, in Brianza.

Giovan Battista Crespi, called Cerano
(Novara?, ca. 1575 – Milan 1632)
Saint Francis in Ecstasy
Oil on canvas, 93·5x74
Donated to Brera in 1969, originally in the Poletti collection.

Giulio Cesare Procaccini
(Bologna 1574 – Milan 1625)
Mystic Marriage of Saint Catherine
Oil on canvas, 149x145
In Brera since 1896, originally in the Archbishop's Palace at Milan (bequest of Cardinal Cesare Monti).

Giulio Cesare Procaccini in collaboration with Cerano and Morazzone
Martyrdom of Saints Rufina and Seconda (*Three-Hand Picture*)
Oil on canvas, 192x192
In Brera since 1896, originally in the Archbishop's Palace at Milan (bequest of Cardinal Cesare Monti).

Giulio Cesare Procaccini
Saint Jerome
Oil on canvas, 165x65
In Brera since 1805, originally in the church of Il Gesù at Pavia.

Giulio Cesare Procaccini
Saint Cecily
Oil on canvas, 165x65
In Brera since 1805, originally in the church of Il Gesù at Pavia.

Cerano
Madonna del Rosario
Oil on canvas, 275x218
In Brera since 1805, originally in the monastery of San Lazzaro.

Francesco Cairo
Portrait of Luigi Scaramuccia
Oil on canvas, 95x73
Acquired in 1806.

Giulio Cesare Procaccini
The Magdalen
Oil on canvas, 135x97
In Brera since 1811, originally in the Archbishop's Palace at Milan (bequest of Cardinal Cesare Monti).

Facing page: Daniele Crespi, *Last Supper*.

PANEM ANGELORVM MANDVCAVIT HOMO

Giulio Cesare Procaccini
in collaboration with
Cerano and Morazzone
*Martyrdom of Saints
Rufina and Seconda*
(*Three-Hand Picture*).

Giulio Cesare Procaccini, *Mystic Marriage of Saint Catherine.*

Room XXXI

In this large room we find a number of pictures by important exponents of Italian baroque painting.
One of the greatest of the Roman baroque painters was certainly Pietro da Cortona, an artist who distinguished himself by his gifts as a decorator and his predilection for sumptuous and complex compositions, as can be seen in the celebrated frescoes in Palazzo Barberini at Rome or the ones in Palazzo Pitti at Florence. Here we can admire his *Madonna and Child with Saints*, a painting that clearly reflects his compositional criteria, based on the presence of architecture, landscapes in the background, and the monumentality of the figures, represented in pleasing colors.
Considerable impetus was given to the spread of the baroque style in Italy by the Dutch painter Pieter Paul Rubens during his stay in the country. Here we can see his large panel depicting the *Last Supper*, for which there is a preparatory drawing in the Pushkin Museum at Moscow. The work can be dated to the latter part of Rubens's career (1631-32) and it is thought that the artist made use of several assistants for the execution of the work, a quite common practice given the large number of commissions that he received in those years.
Another foreigner who spent time in Italy, mostly at Genoa, was Rubens's pupil Anton van Dyck. On show here is his *Madonna and Child with Saint Anthony of Padua*. It is one of the Flemish painter's most Italianized works, along with the *Madonna and Child* in the Kunsthistorisches Museum at Vienna. Critics, who tend to date the painting to around 1630, discern in it the influence of Titian.
One of the first Genoese painters to come under the sway of Rubens and van Dyck's work was Bernardo Strozzi, whose compositions also show the decisive influence of the followers of Caravaggio. Here we can see a canvas depicting the *Young Saint John* by this artist, along with his *Portrait of a Knight of Malta*, a fine example of his portraiture.
One original artist who undoubtedly deserves a significant place in the panorama of eighteenth-century painting is Evaristo Baschenis, a native of Bologna where he lived and worked, in all likelihood, for the whole of his life. His still lifes, set inside kitchens or made up of rigorous compositions of musical instruments, from which figures are excluded, form the guiding thread of his personal artistic research.

Luca Giordano
(Naples 1632 – 1705)
Madonna and Child in Glory and Saints Joseph and Anthony of Padua
Oil on canvas, 365x224
In Brera since 1809, originally in the church of the Spirito Santo at Venice.

Gioacchino Assereto
(Genoa ca. 1600 – 1649)
Circumcision
Oil on canvas, 228x163
In Brera since 1838.

Orazio De Ferrari
(Voltri, Genoa, 1606 – Genoa 1657)
Ecce Homo
Oil on canvas, 95x118
Originally in the Archbishop's Palace at Milan (bequest of Cardinal Cesare Monti).

Anton van Dyck
(Antwerp 1599 – London 1641)
Madonna and Child with Saint Anthony of Padua
Oil on canvas, 189x158
In Brera since 1813 by exchange with the Louvre.

Joachim von Sandrart
(Frankfurt 1606 – Nuremberg 1688)
The Good Samaritan
Oil on canvas, 133x133
Signed and dated 1632.
Acquired in 1830/31.

Jacob Jordaens
(Antwerp 1593 – 1678)
The Sacrifice of Isaac
Oil on canvas, 242x155
In Brera since 1813 by exchange with the Louvre.

Pieter Paul Rubens
(Siegen 1577 – Antwerp 1640)
Last Supper
Oil on panel, 304x250
It was originally located in the chapel of the Holy Sacrament in the church of Saint Rambaud at Malines, above the tomb of the client's father.
The work was completed by two predellas representing the *Entry into Jerusalem* and the *Washing of the Feet*, which are now in the Musée des Beaux-Arts at Dijon.
It came to Brera by exchange with the Louvre, where the painting had been deposited in 1794.

Evaristo Baschenis
(Bergamo 1617 – 1677)
Musical Instruments
Oil on canvas, 60x88
Signed. Acquired in 1912.

Felice Boselli (?)
(Piacenza 1650 – Parma 1732)
Still Life
Oil on canvas, 64x69

Felice Boselli (?)
Still Life with Game
Oil on canvas, 64x68

Bernardo Strozzi
(Genoa 1581 – Venice 1644)
Portrait of a Knight of Malta
Oil on canvas, 129x98
Donated in 1904 by Casimiro Sipriot.

Jan Fyt
(Antwerp 1611 – 1661)
Still Life with Game
Still Life with Game
Oil on canvas, 106x145 (each)
In Brera since 1813, originally in the Gallerie dell'Accademia at Venice.

Joseph Heintz the Younger
(Augusta ca. 1600 – Venice 1678)
Vanitas
Oil on canvas, 130x177
Acquired in 1983.

Evaristo Baschenis
Still Life (Kitchen)
Oil on canvas, 97x145
Signed. Acquired in 1915.

Bernardo Strozzi
The Young Saint John
Oil on canvas, 70x55
In Brera since 1855, bequest from Pietro Oggioni.

Evaristo Baschenis, *Musical Instruments.*

Bernardo Strozzi, *Portrait of a Knight of Malta.*

Pietro Berrettini, called Pietro da Cortona
(Cortona 1596 – Rome 1669)
Madonna and Child with Saints John the Baptist, Felix of Cantalice, Andrew and Catherine
Oil on canvas, 296x205
Signed. In Brera since 1811, originally in the Capuchin church at Amandola (Ascoli Piceno).

Pietro da Cortona, *Madonna and Child with Saints.*

Pieter Paul Rubens, *Last Supper.*

Rooms XXXII and XXXIII

Brera possesses a very large number of works by foreign artists, though they vary considerably in quality and origin. The next two rooms offer a careful selection of this material, which for obvious reasons cannot be shown in its entirety.
The first picture we see is an *Adoration of the Magi* attributed by some to an anonymous Master of Antwerp and dated to 1518, or, in the view of others, to the Master of the Virgo inter Virgines. In either case, the artist owes an obvious debt to Roger van der Weyden, from whom he has drawn a number of formal elements.
This is followed by a triptych of modest dimensions by Jan de Beer, painted around the middle of the sixteenth century for a Venetian church. Perhaps the masterpiece of this artist from Antwerp, it is crowded with figures, architecture and views of landscape set in a composition of refined coloring.
Finally we can see a *Saint Francis in Ecstasy*, ascribed to the workshop of the painter Domenikos Theotokópoulos, called El Greco, who was born in Greece but chose to live and work in Spain. This was one of his favorite subjects and some forty versions of it exist, often painted with the help of assistants.
Room XXXIII houses works by Flemish and Dutch painters of the late sixteenth and seventeenth century. The small painting on copper depicting a *Village* by Jan Brueghel is characteristic of the artist's style, with its virtuoso attention to detail, subtle draftsmanship and lively colors.
Although it is initialed and dated 1632, critics now tend to ascribe the oval *Portrait of a Young Woman* not to Rembrandt but to his school. There has been much debate over the identity of the sitter, but she is now thought to be the painter's wife, or more probably sister. The original version of the picture, painted by the artist himself, is thought to be the *Bust of a Young Woman* in the Museum of Fine Arts at Boston.
The *Portrait of a Lady* – formerly believed to be a *Portrait of Amelia di Solms*, princess of Orange – is by Anton van Dyck. It is a fascinating painting modeled on Rembrandt's *Portrait of Maria de' Medici*, now in the Museo del Prado at Madrid.

Room XXXII

Master of Antwerp of 1518
(Antwerp, 16th century)
Adoration of the Magi
Panel, 106x72

School of Antwerp of the 16th century (Jan de Beer?)
Saint Luke painting the Madonna and Child
Tempera on canvas, 93·5x145
In Brera since 1896, originally in the Archbishop's Palace at Milan (bequest of Cardinal Cesare Monti).

Jan de Beer
(Antwerp, documented from 1504 to 1536)
Adoration of the Magi, Birth of Jesus and *Rest on the Flight into Egypt*
Oil on panel, 156x123 (central panel), 156x58 (each side panel)
In Brera since 1808.

Master of the Half-Length Figures
(Flemish, second half of the 15th century)
Saint Catherine
Oil on panel, 45x36

Herman Rode
(Lubeck, documented from 1485 to 1504)
Portrait of a Man
Oil on panel, 35x27
In Brera since 1855, bequest from Pietro Oggioni.

Domenikos Theotokópoulos, called El Greco
(Candia 1541 – Toledo 1614)
Saint Francis
Oil on canvas, 108x66
Signed.

Room XXXIII

Dirk van Santvoort
(Amsterdam 1610 – 1680)
Portrait of a Young Man
Oil on canvas, 190x120
Signed and dated 1643.
In Brera since 1927.

Anton van Dyck
(Antwerp 1599 – London 1641)
Portrait of a Lady (Amelia of Solms?)
Oil on canvas, 140x107
In Brera since 1813 by exchange with the Louvre.

Pieter Paul Rubens
(Siegen 1577 – Antwerp 1640)
The Nymph Syrinx pursued by Pan
Oil on panel, 33x43
In Brera since 1855, bequest from Pietro Oggioni.

Nicolaus Knüpfer
(Leipzig ca. 1603 – Utrecht 1660)
The Parable of the Rich Man Epulo
Oil on panel, 28x45
In Brera since 1855, bequest from Pietro Oggioni.

Rembrandt Harmenszoon van Rijn
(Leiden 1606 – Amsterdam 1669)
Portrait of the Artist's Sister
Oil on panel, 60x50
Signed and dated 1632.
In Brera since 1813 by exchange with the Louvre.

Jan Philips van Thielen
(Malines 1618 – Boisschot 1667)
Vertumnus and Pomona among Flowers
Oil on canvas, 86x66
Signed and dated 1648.
In Brera since 1822.

Jan van Goyen
(Leiden 1596 – The Hague 1656)
Seascape
Oil on panel, 36x46
In Brera since 1832.

Jan Brueghel the Elder
(Brussels 1568 – Antwerp 1625)
Village
Oil on copper, 21x32
Signed and dated 1617.
In Brera since 1809.

Abraham Goovaerts
(Antwerp 1589 – 1626)
A Wood
Oil on panel, 53x79
Signed and dated 1615.
Donated by Marchese Stampa Soncino in 1876.

Master of Antwerp of 1518, *Adoration of the Magi.*

Below: Jan de Beer, *Adoration of the Magi*, *Birth of Jesus* and *Rest on the Flight into Egypt.*

Anton van Dyck, *Portrait of a Lady (Amelia of Solms?).*

Below left: Rembrandt, *Portrait of the Artist's Sister.*

Below right: Master of the Half-Length Figures, *Saint Catherine.*

Facing page: Master of Antwerp of 1518, *Adoration of the Magi*, detail.

ROOM XXXIV

Here we can see the work of some of the most important Italian artists of the eighteenth century, generally represented by large paintings of religious subjects.
The *Crucifixion* was painted at the end of the 1720s by the Bolognese Giuseppe Maria Crespi, a versatile artist who was also famous for his genre scenes. The picture indicates that Crespi was influenced by the tradition of the historical painting.
The great Venetian art of the eighteenth century, which is more fully documented in the following room, is introduced here by two canvases by Sebastiano Ricci, another many-sided artist who made a decisive contribution to the renewal of Venetian painting, and by Giovan Battista Tiepolo's *Our Lady of Mount Carmel.* Painted for the Venetian church of Sant'Apollinare, this is a powerful work in which the critics detect the influence of Piazzetta's style. At the same time Tiepolo seems to have adopted elements drawn from the great Venetian models of the sixteenth century, such as Veronese (*San Zaccaria Altarpiece*, Venice, Gallerie dell'Accademia).
The two small canvases depicting *The Meeting between King Ratchis of the Longobards and Pope Zachary* and *Saint Willibald asking Pope Gregory III for his Blessing* are by the Neapolitan Francesco Solimena. These were preparatory studies for the frescoes at Montecassino, now destroyed. The work of two more Neapolitan painters is on show in this room. Luca Giordano is represented by a rare *Ecce Homo*, a typical example of the painter's style that is thought to be based on a print by Dürer. The two sketches by Nicola Malinconico show the influence of Solimena.
There is also a *Madonna and Child with Saints* by the Roman painter Pompeo Batoni. An altarpiece of the *Sacra Conversazione* type in a markedly classical style, it was one of the first pictures of a religious subject painted by the artist, who went on to become one of the leading figures in eighteenth-century Roman painting.

Pompeo Batoni
(Lucca 1708 – Rome 1787)
Madonna and Child with Saints Joseph, Zachary, Elizabeth and the Young John
Oil on canvas, 403x288
In Brera since 1806, originally in the church of Santi Cosma e Damiano alla Scala at Milan.

Carlo Innocenzo Carloni
(Scaria d'Intelvi, Como, 1683 – 1775)
The Triumph of Faith
Oil on canvas, 57·5x57·5
Donated in 1936.

Nicola Malinconico
(Naples 1663 – 1721)
Joshua halts the Sun
Oil on canvas, 108x114
Acquired in 1962.

Francesco Solimena
(Canale di Serino, Avellino, 1657 – Barra, Naples, 1747)
Bestowal of the Rule on Saint Benedict (now: *Saint Willibald asking Pope Gregory III for his Blessing before going to Convert the Saxons*)
Oil on canvas, 43x75
In Brera since 1805.

Luca Giordano
(Naples 1634 – 1705)
Ecce Homo
Oil on canvas, 158x155
In Brera since 1979.

Francesco Solimena
Saint Leo the Great going to Meet Attila (now: *The Meeting between King Ratchis of the Longobards and Pope Zachary during the Siege of Perugia*)
Oil on canvas, 43x75
In Brera since 1805.

Nicola Malinconico
The Transport of the Ark of the Covenant
Oil on canvas, 108x102
Acquired in 1962.

Giovan Battista Tiepolo
(Venice 1696 – Madrid 1770)
Our Lady of Mount Carmel and the Souls in Purgatory
Oil on canvas, 210x650
This painting was donated to Brera in 1925 by the Chiesa family. It comes from the church of Sant'Apollinare in Venice, where it had been located in the chapel of the Confraternita del Carmine, an association devoted to praying for the release of souls from Purgatory. The picture shows the Virgin giving the scapular to St. Simon Stock, prior general of the Carmelite order and promoter of what is known as the "Scapular devotion," symbolizing the salvation of the soul.

Martin Knoller
(Steinach 1725 – Milan 1804)
Assumption of the Virgin
Oil on panel, 96x53

Giuseppe Bottani
(Cremona 1717 – Mantua 1784)
Departure of Saint Paula of Rome for the Holy Land
Oil on canvas, 410x231
Signed and dated 1745.
In Brera since 1806, originally in the church of Santi Cosma e Damiano alla Scala at Milan.

Pierre Subleyras
(Saint-Gilles-du-Gard 1699 – Rome 1749)
Saint Jerome
Oil on canvas, 408x232
Signed and dated 1739.
In Brera since 1806, originally in the church of Santi Cosma e Damiano alla Scala at Milan.

Sebastiano Ricci
(Belluno 1659 – Venice 1734)
Saint Cajetan comforting a Dying Man
Oil on canvas, 222x134
Acquired in 1919.

Giuseppe Maria Crespi
(Bologna 1665 – 1747)
Crucifixion
Oil on canvas, 291·5x187
In Brera since 1811, originally in the church of Santa Maria Egiziaca at Bologna.

Ubaldo Gandolfi
(Bologna 1728 – Ravenna 1781)
Saint Francis receiving the Stigmata
Oil on canvas, 263x180
In Brera since 1811, originally in the church of Santo Spirito at Cingoli (Macerata).

Sebastiano Ricci (?)
Martyrdom of Saint Erasmus
Oil on canvas, 118x95
Acquired in 1978/79.

Pierre Subleyras
Christ Crucified with the Magdalen and Saints Eusebius and Philip Neri
Oil on canvas, 408x238
Signed and dated 1744.
In Brera since 1806.

Pompeo Batoni, *Madonna and Child with Saints Joseph, Zachary, Elizabeth and the Young John.*

Francesco Solimena, *Saint Leo the Great going to Meet Attila.*

Above: Giovan Battista Tiepolo, *Our Lady of Mount Carmel and the Souls in Purgatory.*

Room XXXV

This room houses a significant group of eighteenth-century Venetian paintings.
They include Giovanni Battista Piazzetta's *Rebecca at the Well*, one of his best-known pictures in which the critics have seen a reference to a work by Rubens now in the Louvre, further confirmation that the Venetian artist drew his inspiration from elsewhere in Europe as well. Piazzetta's style in this period (second half of the 1720s) was characterized by a light palette and a great freshness of execution, with broad brushstrokes underlining the luminosity of the flesh tones.
The small canvas by Giovan Battista Tiepolo depicts *The Temptations of Saint Anthony*. It is a still juvenile work that shows the chiaroscuro effects typical of his early years.
Giovan Battista Pittoni is represented by the small picture of *Hamilcar getting Hannibal to swear his Hatred of the Romans*, part of a series based on the writings of Livy that is now dispersed. The painting, with a compositional structure in which the architectural space is treated like a piece of theatrical scenery, seems to inaugurate a pattern that would become recurrent in much of his later work.
Alongside paintings of historical, mythological and religious subjects, the Venetian art of the period produced some interesting genre scenes, best represented by the painter Pietro Longhi, and an equally fascinating series of pictures – known as *vedute* – presenting perspective views of the city of Venice. Brera possesses a number of works by the greatest exponents of the *veduta*, such as Canaletto, Bellotto and Guardi. Emblematic of Canaletto's production are two paintings in which the artist seems to have contributed to the birth of the "myth" of Venice, that immortal city whose rarefied purity is underlined by the light (used by the painter as a means of investigating reality). Bernardo Bellotto, who painted the two views of Gazzada, a village in the vicinity of Varese, on show here, also paid great attention to atmospheric effects but, in contrast to his uncle and teacher Canaletto, favored a colder light and more vivid colors, while always taking care over the tiniest detail.

In corridor:
Nicolas de Largillière
(Paris 1656 – 1746)
Portrait of a Lady
Oil on canvas, 82x65
Acquired in 1911.

Giovan Battista Pittoni
(Venice, 1687 – 1767)
Hamilcar getting Hannibal to swear his Hatred of the Romans
Oil on canvas, 41x72
Acquired in 1913.

Giovan Battista Pittoni
Bacchus and Ariadne
Oil on canvas, 70x50
Acquired in 1955.

Pietro Falca, called Pietro Longhi
(Venice 1702 – 1785)
The Tooth-Drawer
Oil on canvas, 50x62
Signed.
Acquired in 1911.

Rosalba Carriera
(Venice 1670 – 1758)
Portrait of a Man
Pastel, 47x42

Pietro Longhi
Family Concert
Oil on canvas, 50x62
Acquired in 1911.

Bernardo Bellotto
(Venice 1720 – Warsaw 1780)
View of the Gazzada
Oil on canvas, 64·5x98·5
Acquired in 1831.

Giovanni Antonio Canal, called Canaletto
(Venice 1697 – 1768)
View of Saint Mark's Basin
Oil on canvas, 53x70
In Brera since 1928.

Giovan Battista Piazzetta
(Venice 1683 – 1754)
Rebecca at the Well
Oil on canvas, 102x137
In Brera since 1916, bequest from Emilio Treves.

Canaletto
View of the Grand Canal
Oil on canvas, 53x70
In Brera since 1928.

Bernardo Bellotto
View of the Gazzada
Oil on canvas, 64·5x98·5
Acquired in 1831.
Along with the other painting in this room, the picture is considered one of Bellotto's masterpieces. Both were painted during the artist's brief stay in Italy (1744-47) prior to his final departure for Dresden.

Francesco Guardi
(Venice 1712 – 1793)
View of the Grand Canal looking toward Santa Chiara
Oil on canvas, 56x75
In Brera since 1855, bequest from Pietro Oggioni.

Francesco Zugno
(Venice 1709 – 1787)
Portrait of a Young Singer
Oil on canvas, 45x38
Acquired in 1932, originally in the collection of Prince Giovannelli at Venice.

Francesco Guardi
View of the Grand Canal looking toward Rialto
Oil on canvas, 56x75
In Brera since 1855, bequest from Pietro Oggioni.

Giovan Battista Tiepolo
(Venice 1696 – Madrid 1770)
Temptations of Saint Anthony
Oil on canvas, 40x47
In Brera since 1929.

Gian Domenico Tiepolo
(Venice 1727 – 1804)
The Battle
Oil on canvas, 52x70
In Brera since 1855, bequest from Pietro Oggioni.

In corridor:
Giovan Domenico Ferretti
(Florence 1692 – 1768)
Self-Portrait
Oil on canvas, 110x85
In Brera since 1811.

Bernardo Bellotto, *View of the Gazzada.*

Above: Canaletto, *View of Saint Mark's Basin.*

Bernardo Bellotto, *View of the Gazzada.*

Above: Francesco Guardi, *View of the Grand Canal looking toward Rialto.*

Pietro Longhi, *The Tooth-Drawer.*

Above left: Rosalba Carriera, *Portrait of a Man.*

Above right: Nicolas de Largillière, *Portrait of a Lady.*

Giovan Battista Piazzetta, *Rebecca at the Well.*

Giovan Battista Tiepolo, *Temptations of Saint Anthony.*

Room XXXVI

In this room we find a series of paintings, mostly of small size, representing some particular sectors of Italian eighteenth-century art.
Examples of so-called genre painting are provided by pictures like the *Porter with Basket* and *Seated Porter* by Giacomo Ceruti, also known by the nickname of Pitocchetto ("Little Beggar") because of his propensity to depict common people with great objectivity and simplicity. These two pendants, among the most significant of the Brescian painter's works, can be dated to around the middle of the 1730s.
We can see the same theme, though interpreted with a different spirit, in the painting of *The Old Woman and the Street Arab* by the Neapolitan Gaspare Traversi, who liked to depict his subjects with lively realism and attention to the study of their characters, often greatly exaggerated.
Another artist who often represented scenes of everyday life, and not just in genre paintings but also in his pictures of religious subjects, was the Bolognese Giuseppe Maria Crespi. Here we can see his *Fair with Tooth Drawer* (very similar to the painting of the same subject in the Uffizi), a work which clearly shows the artist's style, characterized by dense brushwork and a fondness for scenes filled with movement.
There are several examples of eighteenth-century portraits in the room, including the *Portrait of a Gentleman* by Vittore Ghislandi, called Fra Galgario, and the *Portrait of the Artist's Father* by Pietro Ligari.

Giuseppe Maria Crespi, *A Fair.*

Pietro Ligari
(Sondrio 1686 – 1752)
Portrait of the Artist's Father
Oil on canvas, 98x70
Donated in 1831 by Angelo Ligari.

Vittore Ghislandi, called Fra Galgario
(Bergamo 1655 – 1747)
Portrait of the Painter
Oil on canvas, 75x60
In Brera since 1813.

Gaspare Traversi
(Naples ca. 1732 – Rome 1769)
The Old Woman and the Street Arab
Oil on canvas, 80x105
Acquired in 1938.

Giacomo Ceruti, called Pitocchetto
(Brescia 1698 – 1767)
Portrait of a Man
Oil on canvas, 72x53
In Brera since 1872.

Giacomo Ceruti
Seated Porter
Oil on canvas, 130x91
Donated in 1966.

Giacomo Ceruti
Still Life
Oil on canvas, 43x59
Acquired in 1802.

Vittore Ghislandi
Portrait of a Gentleman
Oil on canvas, 127x98
Acquired in 1918.

Giacomo Ceruti
Still Life with Fruit
Oil on canvas, 43x59
Acquired in 1802.

Giacomo Ceruti
Porter with Basket on his Back
Oil on canvas, 130x95
Donated in 1966.

Giuseppe Maria Crespi
(Bologna 1665 – 1747)
Self-Portrait
Oil on canvas, 42x30
Acquired in 1914 from the collection of Benigno Crespi.

Giuseppe Maria Crespi
A Fair with Tooth Drawer
Oil on canvas, 76x84
Acquired in 1916.

Giovan Battista Piazzetta
(Venice 1683 – 1754)
Old Man Praying
Oil on canvas, 46x37
Acquired in 1908.

Anton Raphael Mengs, *Portrait of the Singer Domenico Annibali.*

Above right: Vittore Ghislandi, *Portrait of a Gentleman.*

Alongside: Pietro Ligari, *Portrait of the Artist's Father.*

Francesco Londonio
(Milan 1723 – 1783)
Eight Studies of Figures
Oil on paper, 43x28 (each)
In Brera since 1837, bequest from Carlo Londonio.

In corridor:
Anton Raphael Mengs
(Aussig 1728 – Rome 1779)
Portrait of the Singer Domenico Annibali
Oil on canvas, 125x95
Signed and dated 1750.
Acquired in 1837.

In corridor:
Joshua Reynolds
(Plympton 1723 – London 1792)
Portrait of Lord Donoughmore
Oil on canvas, 100x126
Acquired in 1933.

Giacomo Ceruti, *Porter with Basket on his Back.*

Rooms XXXVII and XXXVIII

The last rooms in the Picture Gallery contain works by nineteenth-century Italian painters.
One of the most important figures in Italian neoclassicism was Andrea Appiani, and here we can see his picture of *Olympus*, which displays a certain academic coldness typical of the latter part of his career.
Among the more famous of the paintings is probably Francesco Hayez's *The Kiss*, a work which reveals the principal components of the style of the founder of Lombard Romanticism, i.e. the influence of Venetian painting – in the sense of a harking back to sixteenth-century artists like Titian and Savoldo – and an abstraction of Purist derivation. Also on show here are some of his portraits, a genre at which he proved particularly skilled, such as the portraits of *Alessandro Manzoni* and the *Stampa Soncino Family*, or the canvas depicting *The Last Moments of Doge Martin Faliero*, a work of intense psychological participation in the personal drama of the historical figure.
Giovanni Fattori, a painter with ties to the *macchiaioli* movement but who retained a degree of independence, is represented here by the *Red Cart* (1887), a picture of great vigor constructed out of a few elements. In stark contrast to the bombastic Risorgimento painting of the time, it speaks of a simple and everyday world of which the artist was very fond.
Another member of the *macchiaioli* movement was Silvestro Lega. Here we see *The Pergola*, a work that celebrates the ideals of a quiet and sheltered life proper to the Tuscan bourgeoisie through the immediacy and truthfulness of the figures and the simple and severe composition.
The Italian movement of Divisionism is represented by Giovanni Segantini's *Spring Pastures*, in which the artist already seems to be moving toward themes of the Symbolist type and shows a tendency toward stylization. Yet the painting stands out for its great luminosity and, above all, the fibrous way in which the paint is laid on.
In room XXXVIII we can see Giuseppe Pellizza da Volpedo's great picture *The Stream*, a work clearly linked to the artist's social interests. After working on it for a long time, the artist left the picture incomplete, though he returned to the same theme in the *Fourth Estate*, now in the Galleria d'Arte Moderna at Milan.
The only work by a twentieth-century artist on show is the Futurist painter Umberto Boccioni's *Self-Portrait*, whose backdrop of suburban areas of the city seems to anticipate the kind of results that the artist would achieve in paintings like *The City Rises*.

Room XXXVII

Martin Knoller
(Steinach 1725 – Milan 1804)
Self-Portrait
Oil on canvas, 97x75
Signed and dated 1803.
Donated in 1806.

Andrea Appiani
(Milan 1754 – 1817)
Self-Portrait
Oil on panel, 19x15
Donated in 1823 by the governor of Lombardy.

Giuseppe Bossi
(Busto Arsizio 1777 – Milan 1817)
Self-Portrait
Oil on panel, 38x30
In Brera since 1841, bequest from Gaetano Cattaneo.

Giuliano Traballesi
(Florence 1727 – Milan 1812)
Self-Portrait
Oil on canvas, 73x95
In Brera since 1806.

Andrea Appiani
Olympus
Oil on canvas, 45x136
Acquired in 1848.

Thomas Lawrence
(Bristol 1769 – London 1830)
Portrait of Antonio Canova
Oil on canvas, 46x36
Acquired in 1873.

Domenico Aspari
(Milan 1745 – 1831)
Self-Portrait
Oil on canvas, 98x74
Painted and donated in 1805.

Francesco Hayez
(Venice 1791 – Milan 1882)
Portrait of the Stampa Soncino Family
Oil on canvas, 125x108
In Brera since 1900, bequest from Stefano Stampa.

Marco Gozzi
(San Giovanni Bianco, Bergamo, 1759 – Bergamo 1839)
Landscape in Valsesia
Oil on canvas, 80x57
In Brera since 1818.

Pierre Paul Prud'hon
(Cluny 1758 – Paris 1823)
Portrait of Count Giovan Battista Sommariva
Oil on canvas, 210x156
In Brera since 1873.

Francesco Hayez
Mary Stuart being Told of her Death Sentence
Panel, 45x58
Signed and dated 1827.

Federico Faruffini
(Sesto San Giovanni 1831 – Perugia 1869)
Sordello and Cunizza
Oil on canvas, 85x116
Acquired in 1865.

Francesco Hayez
The Kiss
Oil on canvas, 112x90
In Brera since 1886, bequest from Alfonso Maria Visconti. The work was shown for the first time at Brera in 1859, where it proved such a success that the artist was obliged to produce several other versions. The message of individual and patriotic love conveyed by the painting made it an extremely popular subject, much in demand at a particular time in Italian history, on the eve of the country's unification.

Francesco Hayez
Portrait of Teresa Borri Stampa
Oil on canvas, 117x92

Andrea Appiani, *Olympus.*

Signed and dated 1849.
In Brera since 1900, Stampa bequest.

Francesco Hayez
Flowers
Oil on canvas, 124x95
In Brera since 1883, bequest from the artist.

Francesco Hayez
The Last Moments of Doge Marin Faliero
Oil on canvas, 238x192
Signed and dated 1867.
Donated to the Accademia di Brera by the artist in 1867.

Francesco Hayez
Portrait of Alessandro Manzoni
Oil on canvas, 118x92
In Brera since 1900, Stampa bequest.

Francesco Hayez
Melancholy
Oil on canvas, 138x101
In Brera since 1889, bequest from Filippo Ala Ponzoni.

Giovanni Segantini
(Arco di Trento, 1858 – Schafberg 1899)
Spring Pastures
Oil on canvas, 98x155
Signed and dated 1896.
Donated in 1957 by the Friends of Brera.

Federico Zandomeneghi
(Venice 1841 – Paris 1917)
The Curl
Oil on canvas, 79x47
On deposit from the Civica Galleria d'Arte Moderna in Milan since 1950.

Filippo Carcano
(Milan 1840 – 1914)
The Game of Billiards
Oil on canvas, 76x108
Signed. Acquired in 1867.

Giovanni Fattori
(Livorno 1825 – Florence 1908)
The Red Cart
Oil on canvas, 88x179
Signed. In Brera since 1937, originally in the Gualino collection at Turin.

Silvestro Lega
(Modigliana, Forlì, 1826 – Florence 1895)
The Pergola
Oil on canvas, 72x92
Signed and dated 1868.
Donated in 1931 by the Friends of Brera.

Giovanni Estienne
(Florence 1840 – after 1892)
The Third National Shooting Championship in Florence
Oil on canvas, 56x46
Donated in 1951 by Paolo Stramezzi.

Giovanni Fattori
Prince Amedeus wounded at Custoza
Oil on canvas, 100x265
Acquired in 1872 at the Esposizione Nazionale di Belle Arti in Milan.

ROOM XXXVIII

Giuseppe Pellizza da Volpedo
(Volpedo, Alessandria, 1868 – 1907)
The Stream
Oil on canvas, 241x427
Donated in 1986.
Preceded by a series of sketches, drawings and cartoons collectively known as the *Ambassadors of Hunger* (1891-94), the huge canvas, painted between 1895 and 1897, marks a fundamental stage in the artist's career, when he succeeded in giving an artistic dimension to the humanitarian ideals and progressive impulses that were so prominent in end-of-the-century culture.
The theme of class struggle and the emancipation of workers touched on in the *Stream* was given a definitive treatment in the *Fourth Estate* (1898-1901), now in Milan's Civica Galleria d'Arte Moderna.

Umberto Boccioni
(Reggio Calabria 1882 – Verona 1916)
Self-Portrait
Oil on canvas, 70x100
Signed and dated 1908.
Donation of 1951.

Francesco Hayez, *The Last Moments of Doge Marin Faliero.*

Francesco Hayez, *Portraits of Teresa Borri Stampa* and *Alessandro Manzoni.*

Francesco Hayez, *Flowers.*

Francesco Hayez, *The Kiss*.

Giovanni Fattori, *The Red Cart.*

Above: Silvestro Lega, *The Pergola.*

Giovanni Estienne, *The Third National Shooting Championship in Florence.*
Federico Zandomeneghi, *The Curl.*

Umberto Boccioni, *Self-Portrait.*

Above: Giuseppe Pellizza da Volpedo, *The Stream.*

THE JESI COLLECTION

The important collection of Emilio and Maria Jesi – highly representative of the tastes of collectors in the 1930s and 1940s – was donated to the Pinacoteca di Brera in 1976. This first donation, comprising fifty-six works, was followed in 1984 by a second one (made up of another sixteen pieces). Both were made by Maria Jesi in memory of her husband and at his specific behest.
Thanks to this, the Picture Gallery now possesses a collection of modern art of the highest quality. It is currently displayed in a corridor at the beginning of the tour of the museum, until a more suitable location can be found. The Jesi collection includes not only pictures by Italian artists active chiefly between 1910 and 1940, but also a number of works by painters of international renown, such as Picasso, Braque, Bonnard, Severini and Modigliani. Here we can see Amedeo Modigliani's *Portrait of a Young Woman*, painted in 1915, while Gino Severini's work is represented by the canvases *Le Nord-Sud* (1912), *Still Life with Squash* (1917) and *Still Life with Fruit Bowl* (1918).
The Futurist movement, with its faith in progress and its glorification of the frenzy of modern life, is documented by the famous picture of the *Brawl in Gallery*, painted by Umberto Boccioni in 1911, as well as by his study for the equally celebrated canvas *The City Rises* (1910-11), now in the Museum of Modern Art at New York. An example of the Futurist phase of Carlo Carrà's work is provided by the painting *Rhythms of Objects*, completed by the artist in 1911.
Metaphysical painting, with its interest in the irrational and the formal elaboration of articles of everyday use and its predilection for the recondite, is represented by Carrà's *Mother and Son*, *Metaphysical Muse* and *Enchanted Chamber*.
We can also admire several *Still Lifes* by Giorgio Morandi, emblematic of this painter's highly personal style. In addition, the Jesi collection comprises paintings by artists belonging to the Roman School, the "Novecento" movement and other currents from the early part of the twentieth century.
The group of paintings by Morandi (*Pink and Blue Flowers*, 1916; *Still Life*, 1921) and De Pisis (*Still Life with Eggs*, 1924; *Sacred Fish*, 1925; *View of Paris*) is particularly interesting.
Finally, the Jesi collection includes a fascinating group of sculptures. Among them are three wax figures by Medardo Rosso, an important Italian artist of the second half of the nineteenth century. Entitled *La petite rieuse*, *L'enfant juif*, and *La femme à la voilette*, they are representative of the sculptor's attempts at a fusion of figure and surroundings.
There are some characteristic works, such as *The Drinker*, by Arturo Martini, one of the most significant Italian sculptors of the first half of the twentieth century, while the sculptor and painter Marino Marini, who often worked to commissions from the Jesi, is represented by the *Pomona lying down* and the monumental bronze *The Miracle. Horse and Horseman*.

Umberto Boccioni,
The City Rises.

Umberto Boccioni, *Brawl in Gallery.*

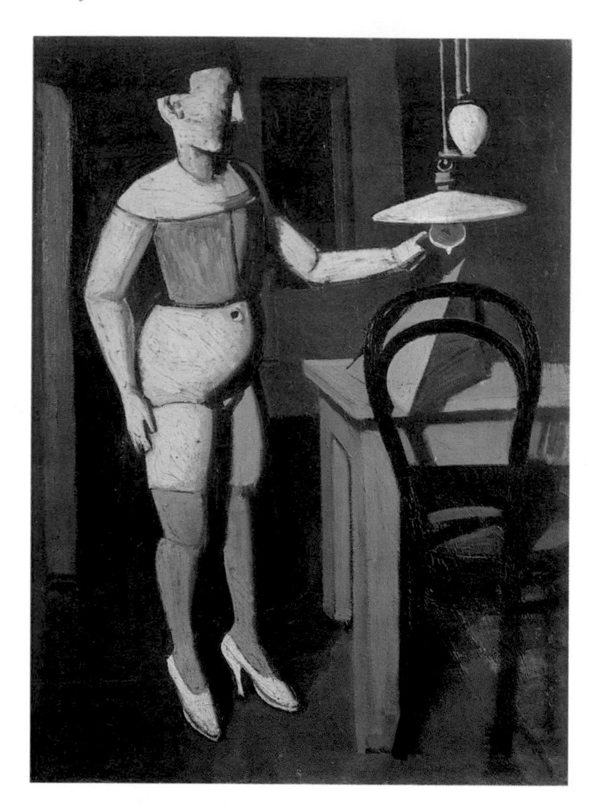

Gino Severini, *Le Nord-Sud.*

Above left: Mario Sironi, *The Lamp.*

Above right: Giorgio Morandi, *Metaphysical Still Life with Set Square.*

Carlo Carrà, *Metaphysical Muse.*

Index of artists

Translation: Christopher Evans
Editing: Marilena Vecchi
Photographic acknowledgements: SCALA ARCHIVE
(R. Bencini, M. Falsini, U. Marzani, M. Sarri)
Printed by: "Arti Grafiche" Stampa Nazionale, Calenzano (Florence), 2001